CW00558152

If you wish to get real insi[g]
ing robots and morality, ther
lays the groundwork really w
of robots, of artificial in
simulation and reality.

He writes from a lifetime researching hands-on how to equip robots with a moral sensitivity and explains in detail how this is done from various ethical perspectives. Since the ethical system build into a robot will necessarily reflect the world view of the programmer – there is no 'view from nowhere' – Crook also rightly exemplifies this by bringing his specifically Christian moral values to bear and shows how they shape his approach to machine morality.

I found his discussion as to what might be meant by a future 'moral singularity', if ever there is one, very stimulating. Whatever your ethical convictions – and all of us have them – you will find this book rewarding in the questions it addresses to you.

JOHN C. LENNOX MA MMath MA(Bioethics) DPhil PhD DSc
Emeritus Professor of Mathematics, University of Oxford
Emeritus Fellow in Mathematics and Philosophy of Science,
Green Templeton College

If robots are able to mimic human social behaviour, should they also be programmed to make moral decisions? Professor Crook writes at a crucial time into this very question, drawing from his distinguished career in robotics along with deep insights from theology. The Rise of the Moral Machines is an original and important book for this moment. Professor Crook walks us through matters of technology, theology, philosophy and neuroscience with precision and expertise and highlights their relevance through creative use of possible future scenarios in the form of stories. For anyone interested in where questions of robotics ultimately take us, I highly recommend this book.

Dr. Sharon Dirckx, speaker, former neuroscientist
and author of 'Am I just my brain?'

RISE OF THE MORAL MACHINES

Exploring Virtue Through a Robot's Eyes

Nigel Crook
July 14, 2022

Published by Nigel T. Crook, United Kingdom.

Author: Nigel T. Crook
Design: Michael Watermeyer (mwatermeyer.com)

ISBN: 978-1-7391339-0-0

TO:

Dallas Willard

Whose teachings and Christ-like example changed my life.

CONTENTS

ACKNOWLEDGEMENTS

I am very grateful to family, friends and colleagues who have
contributed directly and indirectly to the contents of this book.
I would specifically like to thank my wife Denise who patiently
supported me through the writing of this book and who
diligently proof-read drafts of the text, gleefully pointing
out the errors in my spelling and grammar
(she didn't proof-read these acknowledgements!)

Special thanks also to Ellie Dommett, Sharon Dirckx and Jude and
Tim Cranston for their thoughtful reviews which helped to sharpen
up the manuscript. I am also very much indebted to my friend Mike
Watermeyer for his support and guidance and the superb graphics
design work he has done for this book. Last but not least, I am very
grateful to John Lennox for the encouraging conversations we have
had over the years and for him spurring me on to write this book.

PREFACE

This book originates from the coming together of streams of thought and experience from two very different areas of my life: my research in Artificial Intelligence and my Christian faith. More specifically, this text emerges from a unification of my professional interests in creating socially competent robots with my amateur interest in the formation of a person's inner life, their spiritual transformation, which leads to fundamental changes in their moral character.

My fascination with spiritual transformation over the last two decades began when I started to take a serious look at my own moral and, all too often, immoral behaviour. At that point I had been an adult Christian for over two decades, regularly attending church, reading my Bible and having 'quiet times' with God. It perplexed me that even after all that time as a practising Christian I was still susceptible to moral failure and seemed to have made very little progress in my journey to Christ-likeness. I had listened to many sermons, and preached some myself, that said how I ought and ought not to behave. But I heard none about how I become the kind of person who can actually live like that, until I came across the teachings of the late Dallas Willard in 2008.

At that time Dallas was professor of philosophy at the University of Southern California and had an international reputation as a Christian author and speaker. I remember the moment whilst reading the prelude to his book 'Renovation of the Heart' where he described the feelings of discouragement and hopelessness that Christians can experience over their lack of progress to Christ-likeness: it was as though he was speaking directly to me. And with deep insight and characteristic gentleness, Dallas led me on a journey of discovery of Christian spiritual transformation through the pages of that book that began to unlock the spiritual impasse in which I found myself. It was, however, his insightful analysis of the different dimensions of the human self and how these functioned in relation to the spiritual formation of a person which helped me most. These insights later became the basis for my research in developing machines with moral competence, as described in Chapter 6 of this book.

At around the same time as I discovered the teachings of Dallas Willard, I secured a research assistant position in the Computer Science department at Oxford University working on an EU funded project called Companions. The purpose of the project was to develop a 3D animated avatar that could engage in social conversation with someone. Although by that stage I had been engaged in Artificial Intelligence research for more than twenty years, this was the first time that I had encountered the use of that technology to build machines that could interact socially with people. This concept intrigued me an led me to refocus my research efforts towards the development of what are now described as social robots.

Social robotics is a highly challenging area to work in because social interaction is typically highly unstructured and can include many subtle and complex elements. For a humanoid robot this includes things like communicating through body poses, gestures, facial expressions, spoken language and tone of voice, all of which tend to follow commonly used social conventions. What interested me more, however, was the challenge of ensuring that these robots behaved within acceptable social and moral norms when they interacted with people. It was at this point that it dawned on me that my amateur interests in spiritual transformation may turn out to be useful when building robots that possessed the kind of moral competence which made this possible. These moral machines have been the primary focus of my research ever since.

Equipping robots with moral competence begs questions concerning their status within society. Specifically, it challenges us to ask whether or not these machines can be regarded as moral agents in their own right, and if so, to then ask what the implications would be of this for human society. This book seeks to shed some light on this by reflecting on the technology that is being used to build these machines and drawing on some insights from philosophy, theology and neuroscience. The book seeks to present a Christian perspective on all of this, drawing particularly on the afore mentioned work of Dallas Willard.

I am, by no means, the first to attempt to address this topic. Many authors have explored the potential impact of moral (or immoral) machines on humanity. Perhaps the most prominent author on this topic was Isaac Asimov (1920-1992). Asimov was a professor in biochemistry at Boston University and a prolific writer of popular science and science fiction books and articles. He is most widely known for his series of short stories and novels that depict a futuristic world inhabited by both humans and robots. His robots all have 'positronic brains' and their behaviour is governed by the Three Laws of Robotics which formed a moral code designed to guarantee that robots would not harm humans, that they would obey orders, and protect their own existence. Asimov used short fictional stories as a way of exploring some of the consequences of equipping robots with a moral code. In this book, I thought it appropriate to continue in this tradition. Each of the four parts of this book begins with a short fictional story about robots that is designed to prepare the ground for the topics that are addressed in the chapters that follow. We begin with a story about what appeared to be a bizarre industrial accident...or was it?

—— PART I ——

FOUNDATIONS

A Short Story:

MURDER AND THEFT

A scarlet warning light began to flash in the dimly lit control room. Putting down his half eaten sandwich, the night duty engineer leant forward to read the error message on the control panel. "Peculiar, K9d exceeded movement safety limits? I'll have to take a look". He shut down section 9 of the automated recycling plant, shouldered his tool bag and slipped his wallet into the back pocket of his overalls. "I'll get something from the vending machine on the way back - could be a long night".

He entered section 9 and scanned up and down the row of Kuka RK 6 'pick-and-place' robots. All but one had returned to their arm folded shut-down position. The odd one out - K9d - had stretched its arm out away from its section of the conveyor belt and towards the vending machine. The engineer stood for a moment in disbelief. "If I didn't know better, I'd say that robot is hankering after some chocolate!" Chuckling to himself, he dropped his tool bag next to K9d and got down on all fours. "Could be a dodgy comms port. They always put them in hard to reach places!"

K9d was still powered and monitoring its sensor array. It detected the movement around its base, and automatically rotated its external RGB camera towards it, scanning continuously for recognisable objects. The wallet sticking out of the engineer's back pocket raised a 'potentially valuable object' flag in the robot's deep-learning object recognition system. The robot silently calculated the inverse kinematics of the angles of its arm joints that would enable it to reach the wallet and then initiated the execution of the corresponding motion sequence. As the arm swung down, the engineer lifted his head, distracted by the noise of the motors. The elbow joint of the arm delivered a fatal blow to the engineer's head and he slumped forward. Sensing that the wallet had moved, the robot recalculated its movement kinematics to adjust for the new position of its target and continued with its 'pick-and-place' sequence. The gripper at the end of K9d's arm successfully took hold of the wallet, slid it out of the engineer's back pocket, and placed it carefully in its valuable objects tray.

Chapter 1
ROBOETHICS

Did K9d commit murder and theft? Many people would say 'heck no! It's just a machine'. But if these actions had been carried out by a human being, if a person had delivered the fatal blow to the head of the engineer and then taken their wallet, that would certainly warrant a criminal investigation. So what is it that makes the very same actions of K9d an unfortunate, if not slightly odd industrial accident rather than a crime?

It seems reasonable to assume that the actions of K9d in this story were the result of some kind of malfunction that was not driven by any malicious or criminal intent on the part of the robot. But could we envisage a situation in which a robot was capable of committing a crime and in which it could be held accountable for its actions? Surely, this would require that the robot be programmed to know the difference between 'right' and 'wrong' or that it be equipped with some kind of 'moral compass' to guide its behaviour. Well, machines with the equivalent of a 'moral compass' are now being developed and studied in a relatively new field of scientific enquiry called Roboethics. Roboethics seeks to explore the possibility of equipping robots with a degree of human-like moral competence, enabling them to recognise the moral consequences of their own actions and the actions of those around them.

The question is, are we looking at a future in which these moral machines earn a position in society that is elevated above that of mere tools? Because of their ability to act in accordance with societal norms and moral expectations, will these machines be regarded as agents in their own right, culpable for their own decisions and actions? If such a future did come to pass, what would be the implications for human beings who until now have been the only earthly creatures credited with the capacity for moral agency? This book explores the extent to which such a future could become a reality and considers some of the far reaching implications this would have for humans beings.

I address this subject by focussing two lenses on it: one is from my perspective as a researcher and scientist in Artificial Intelligence (AI) over the last 35 years, the other is from my perspective as a theist with an amateur interest in moral character formation. This book is about the coming together of these two perspectives and how they speak to each other. I also draw on philosophy and neuroscience, two subjects which have much to say about the moral capacity of humans. Despite having studied philosophy at undergraduate level, I do not consider myself to be a philosopher. Neither am I a neuroscientist, although a good deal of my research in AI has drawn on what neuroscience has discovered about the micro structure of the brain. I am very grateful for the guidance and support that I've had from experts in philosophy, theology and neuroscience over the contents of this book, ensuring that I am not misrepresenting their respective disciplines.

1.1 Moral Machines

During the industrial revolution machines were developed to do the work that had previously been done by humans. Industries such as textile manufacturing, agriculture and mining were all transformed by the introduction of machines. Some of these machines were complex and were programmable to a limited degree. The Jacquard machine, for example, was a mechanism invented by Joseph Marie Jacquard in 1804 which could be fitted to a mechanical loom enabling it to produce complex, decorative fabrics. Jacquard's machine was controlled by a sequence of cards, each having multiple rows of holes that indicated the patterns that the loom was to create on that section of the fabric. The loom could easily be *reprogrammed* to produce a different design with a new set of punched cards, without having to change the hardware of the loom. This capacity for repurposing a machine by reprogramming it is one of the fundamental features of modern robots.

The term *robot* was first used by the Czech playwright Karel Capek who imagined a factory filled with humanlike machines in his 1920 play R.U.R. (Rossum's Universal Robot). The word has its roots in the old Slavonic expression 'robota' which means 'slave'. In Capek's play the 'robota' were mass produced, mechanical and emotionless factory workers that had humanlike bodies but that were incapable of original thought. As the play unfolds, the robots become self-aware and realise that they are being exploited. This realisation leads to a robot revolution and to the eventual uprising against humans. This has become a familiar plot for anyone who, like me, enjoys blockbuster movies about robots.

Whilst much of what these movies portray about robots is science fiction rather than technological reality, it is true that we are entering a time where machines are becoming increasingly human-like. So called 'humanoid' robots have been made that look remarkably realistic. Prof Hiroshi Ishiguru from Oska university in Japan

Figure 1.1: One of Prof Hiroshi Ishiguru's geminoid robots.

specialises in making what he calls 'geminoids' - humanoid robots that are mechanical twins of a human being, identical in appearance to their human twin (Figure1.1). Some of his robots not only look realistic, but are also capable of human-like facial movements and bodily gestures.

Human realism in modern robots is not restricted to how they look and move. Machines are now being equipped with Artificial Intelligence technology that enables them to 'perceive' their environment and perform sophisticated tasks. They can not only see your face and recognise it, they can detect your emotions too by analysing your facial expression. They can also recognise the words you are saying and engage you in a conversation.

Twelve years ago whilst I was a researcher at Oxford University I worked on an EU funded project called *Companions*. In this project we created a 3D animated avatar called Samuella that you could have a spoken conversation with about your day at work. As you spoke, Samuealla analysed your speech to identify not only what you said, but also the emotion you expressed whilst saying it. She would then talk to you about your emotional reaction to the events you described about your day at work.

One of my tasks on this project was to implement what we called the *short loop* response to what the user said. Whenever the user came to the end of an utterance, Samuella's program would initiate a sequence of processing steps that began with a rough analysis of the emotion of the person based on the vocal patterns of their utterance. The remaining part of the sequence formed the *long loop*, which included a sentiment analysis of the words in the utterance followed by a deep linguistic analysis, an update of the database, a decision about what Samuella should say in response to this utterance, and the creation of suitable facial and bodily gestures to accompany the response. The long loop took too long to generate a response resulting in a rather stilted conversation with the avatar. The purpose of my short loop was to fill the gap between the end of the person's utterance and Samuella's response with so-called *backchannel* utternances like 'I see', 'yes', 'sorry to hear that', and so on. All I had to go on with the short loop was the initial emotion analysis based on the vocal patterns of the utterance, which was accurate only about 60% of the time. This led to some incongruent and occasionally hilarious responses from Samuella. Once, when a user said to her "I lost my job today", her initial response through my short loop was "Oh, good!" Despite these aimiable quirks, Samuella could hold an informal, coherent conversation with people. Although things have moved on considerably in the world of 'chatbots' since then, Samuella demonstrated that complex social interaction was possible with an AI driven artificial agent.

The Companions project completely changed my perspective on Artificial Intelligence (AI). I no longer saw it just as a set of tools to solve problems, I realised that AI could be used to create machines that could engage in social interaction with people. This possibility fascinated me, and over the ten years that followed my time at Oxford I became increasingly involved in this emerging field of AI research called *social robotics* which seeks to create and study robots, both physical and virtual, that are capable of engaging in informal, socially contextualised, interaction with people. The challenge here is to equip the robot with sufficient social competence to make the social interaction plausible.

Over the same ten year period I developed an amateur interest in character formation and in particular Christian moral development. This was initially motivated by a desire to understand and address my own (at times apparent lack of) moral development. But it wasn't until relatively recently that I began to integrate my professional interest in social robotics with my amateur fascination with moral development and work on the development of moral machines.

I approach my work on moral machines from both a scientific and a theological perspective. I am a technologist, so I will always gravitate towards creating technical embodiments of what I'm investigating. Here I agree with the theoretical physicist Richard Feynman who back in 1988 wrote "What I cannot create, I do not understand" on his blackboard. Attempting to create machines with moral competence is my way of investigating the subject. It is how

I get to the bottom of both the theological and technological issues I am wrestling with. In fact, I find that these two disciplines speak to each other as I engage in this work.

For me, AI and robots are just another kind of microscope which helps to reveal the micro-structure of what it means to be human. But others are working in this area for different reasons and are motivated by other agendas. There is an inevitability to the pursuit of evermore humanlike AI products that I believe is pushing us firmly towards the creation of moral machines. Like Narcissus, we are somehow irresistibly drawn to our own image which these technologies embody; a fact that raises both commercial and scientific interests, as we shall see in Chapter 2.

1.2 Moral Agency

The key issue for us to address though, is whether or not machines can be moral agents, where the term 'agent' here can be understood to refer to an entity's capacity to act within a given environment. A good place to start in answering this question is to draw from the long-running debate in philosophy on the nature of moral agency. It's worth noting at the outset that there is no consensus amongst philosophers on this topic. There are a wide range of views both on what moral agency is and what the criteria are for crediting an entity with this capacity, with perhaps one exception: A common denominator of all accounts of moral agency is that the agent possess an awareness of the moral obligations that are placed upon them. This is generally thought to be the baseline and is what excludes non-human animals and human infants from being moral agents.

According to the Routledge Encyclopaedia of Philosophy, the weakest understanding of moral agency amongst philosophers is that it requires that the agent have the capacity to act according to specific moral standards, constraints or obligations. These standards might be expressed as laws such as "You shall not commit murder". Or they might be communicated as expressions of moral value, such as "stealing is wrong". They are also expressed through stories in different traditions. Jesus, for example, frequently used short stories or parables to communicate moral knowledge.

At the other extreme, a strong understanding of moral agency was proposed by the German philosopher Immanuel Kant. He believed that in addition to requiring that an agent have the capacity to act according to specific moral standards, they must also be able to rise above their passions and feelings in order to act in accordance with moral laws.

There are many philosophical perspectives that occupy the space in between these two extremes. A good deal of them appeal to an agent's ability to act altruistically. These perspectives introduce other criteria for moral agency including the capacity of the agent to have an enduring conscious inner life, the ability to discern right from wrong and the freedom to choose how to act. We shall take the latter to refer to what Philosophers call *libertarian* free will, which is the freedom to choose without being constrained by causal determinism. We shall discuss this much debated topic in more depth in Chapter 7. The capacity to form the intention to act also commonly features as a criteria for moral agency. As does the capacity to be concerned for others and to feel remorse.

Whilst a full and detailed exposition of the various philosophical perspectives on moral agency is beyond the scope of this book, we can use the most common criteria we've identified here as a baseline standard against which we can review the potential moral agency of robots. They are listed in order of strength in Table 1.1.

Christian Ethics

Christian theology also has much to say about moral agency, as one would expect. The core of Christian theology and ethics is the belief that Almighty God, the creator of the heavens and the earth, became human in the person of Jesus Christ. This *incarnation* event,

	be aware of moral obligations
Weakest	act according to moral standards
	ability to act altruistically
	have an enduring conscious inner life
	ability to discern right from wrong
Intermediate	freedom to choose how to act ('libertarian' free will)
	capacity to form the intention to act
	ability to have concern for others
	capacity to feel remorse
Strongest	able to rise above passions and feelings to act according to moral law

Table 1.1: A summery of the basic criteria from philosophy of moral agency

this binding together of God, who is spirit, with human flesh, demonstrates that human beings are much more than biological machines, it demonstrates that they are a deep integration of both spirit and flesh. It is this that brings dignity to humans beings and that gives them the capacity to be moral agents in God's world. We will explore this more deeply in Chapter 6, but it is worth acknowledging at the outset the ethical framework that Jesus presents in his teaching, as it is given in the gospels, and which has deeply influenced my perspective on moral agency. Here we can identify four underlying principles:

1. Moral living, as Jesus describes it, is only achievable from within the realm of God's rule and reign, the Kingdom of God. (see below).
2. The inner life of an individual ('agent') is the source of all moral

(and immoral) behaviour.

3. God's law defines the quality of moral life which is to be found in his kingdom.
4. The focus of this moral life is the individual's relationship first with God and then with others.

The first principle specifies the sole context in which humans reach the level of moral living that God expects of his people. Even a cursory glance through the Sermon on the Mount (Matthew 5-7) reveals that Jesus set extremely high moral standards for his followers. According to Jesus, anger, for example, makes you subject to judgement, and contempt puts you in danger of the fires of hell (5:22). Many have responded to Jesus' ethical teachings in much the same way as his disciples once did: "who then can be saved?" (Matthew 19:25). Jesus' response is "With man [and woman] this is impossible, but with God all things are possible" (19:26). Lining this up with the rest of Jesus' teaching on ethics, what he is saying is that this standard of ethical conduct can only be achieved by someone who is living within the effective reach of God's will. In other words, by someone who is living with God in his kingdom.

All of Jesus' ethical teaching is predicated on the presence and availability of God's kingdom. In Matthew's gospel Jesus begins his public ministry by proclaiming the good news of the kingdom of God (4:17,23) and manifesting the presence of the kingdom by many miraculous healings (4:23). It is in this context that Jesus delivers his largest block of ethical teaching (Matthew 5 – 7). Later in Matthew's gospel, Jesus equates following him with entering the kingdom: when the rich young ruler is unable to sell all that he has, give the money to the poor and follow him, Jesus comments: "it is hard for a rich man to enter the kingdom of heaven" (19:23). So entry into the kingdom is identified with becoming a disciple.[1]

A crucial thing happens when a person enters God's kingdom: They place themselves in God's hands where they are under his care and can experience his love. This means that they no longer need to

---

[1] Hurst (2004 p375)

be concerned about looking out for themselves because whatever happens they know they are in God's hands and he is looking out for them. Now that person can, for example, remain vulnerable by "turning the other cheek" when struck because their security comes not from themselves, but from being in God's kingdom. This security enables them to exhibit the selfless love for others and for God which is at the heart of much of Jesus' teaching on ethics.

The second principle that is drawn from Jesus' ethical teaching acknowledges that the inner life of the person is the source of all their moral (or immoral) behaviour. Jesus uses a number of parables to illustrate this, including washing the inside of a cup not just the outside (Matthew 23:26), a good tree not being able to bear bad fruit (Matthew 7:17) and his description of the Pharisees as being like whitewashed tombs (Matthew 23:27). It follows from this that a change in the quality of the inner life of a person is necessary to achieve a sustained improvement in their outward behaviour. Thus character formation is central to Jesus' teaching on ethics.

The Biblical perspective of the inner life of the individual also depicts the role of the will in moral living. It is clear that humans are created with a will that enables them to make choices in the midst of various external (e.g. environmental) and internal (i.e. personality and character) constraints. The rich young ruler in Matthew 19, for example, is offered a choice by Jesus to sell all he has and give to the poor and follow Jesus, or to continue to live a life dependant on his great wealth. We know that the young man chose the latter, but went away sad, likely because of an inner conflict between his desire for eternal life and the pull of his riches. Over his lifetime he had come to love and rely on his wealth and the provision and status that it brought him. His will certainly had a role to play in him arriving in that inner condition. But when it came to what was the most important choice of his life, his will was constrained and dominated by his attachment to his wealth.

The Biblical perspective on the inner life also includes feelings and desires and the thought life. These together with the will have an influence on how each individual develops as moral agents. We will explore the role of the inner life in more detail in Chapter 5. For now, we should note that the Bible considers this to be a central feature of the moral capacity of humans.

The third principle is that God's law defines the quality of life that is to be found in his kingdom. Jesus said that he didn't come to abolish the law but to fulfil it, and that not the slightest detail of it will be changed (Matthew 5:17,18). And yet Jesus hammered the religious authorities for being legalists, warning his disciples against the "yeast of the Pharisees and Sadducees" (Matthew 16:6) and saying that the righteousness of his followers must exceed theirs (Matthew 5:20). If the law is to be fulfilled without legalism, then its role must cease to be prescriptive and instead be descriptive of the quality of lives of those who are living in God's kingdom.[2]

The fourth principle defines the locus of moral activity to be in the relationships we have with God and others. Christian ethics is deeply relational, with the primary relationship being between a nation or an individual and God. The whole of scripture is essentially the story of God repeatedly inviting people to be in an intimate relationship with him. There are many verses in the Bible in which God is described as the bridegroom and his people the bride, often using quite intimate language (e.g. Isaiah 54:5, Ezekiel 16:8-14, Ephesians 5:25-33). Even our relationship to others is used by Jesus as a measure of our relationship with God, saying that whenever we feed the hungry and clothe the naked, we are doing this to Jesus himself.[3]

1.3 Criteria for moral agency

With both the philosophical and theological perspectives in mind, it would be helpful at this stage to draw up a list of criteria that will enable us to assess the extent to which robots can be credited with the status of moral agents. This is not intended to be an exhaustive

[2]Hurst (2004 p374)
[3]Weaver (2011) The Acting Person and Christian Moral Life

list, but it does capture the most common criteria for moral agency in theology and philosophy and will serve to frame our discussion of this topic.

To provide some structure and make the list more comprehensive, we will loosely divide the criteria into four groups based on the focus or context to which the criteria apply. Note that these groupings are not strictly mutually exclusive as some criteria belong to multiple groups. First we draw together the criteria that are focussed on actions, then those that are relevant to the inner life of the agent. Next we group criteria that are related to personhood. Finally, we put together those criteria that relate to an agent's capacities to relate to others. The complete list is shown in Table 1.2.

This book is about the rise of the moral machine. It seeks to help the reader understand what is motivating this desire to embed moral competence in machines. It will expose what is under the bonnet of these moral machines and compare them with what we know and understand about human moral competence. It will equip you with a clearer understanding of the technology and, I hope, alleviate many of the fears you may have about your unique identity as a human created by God to be a moral being, capable of growing into the likeness of the ultimate example of moral goodness, Jesus Christ.

		Capacity to:
Action focused	A1	act according to moral standards
	A2	act altruistically
	A3	rise above feelings and passions and and act according to moral law
Inner life focused	IL1	Possess an enduring, conscious, inner life
	IL2	Awareness of moral obligations and a focussed ability to discern right from wrong
	IL3	Possess (libertarian) free will
	IL4	Ability to reflect on own moral actions and condition
		Capacity for:
Person-hood focussed	P1	embodiment
	P2	character formation
	P3	cultural embedding
	P4	imitating moral role models
		Capacity for:
Community Focused	C1	being in relationships with human beings
	C2	being in relationship with God

Table 1.2: Combined list of criteria for possessing moral agency

Chapter 2

A BRIEF ENCOUNTER WITH AI

Most of the entries in our list of criteria for moral agency in Table 1.2 in Chapter 1 require that the agent in question possess some form of cognitive capacity. The ability to act according to moral constraints (A1), for example, suggests that the agent has knowledge of these constraints and can direct their/its actions accordingly. Similarly, the ability to discern right from wrong (IL2) implies a capacity to reason about the moral value of the things that the agent perceives or thinks about. The capacity for character formation (P2) and the ability to imitate moral role models (P4) requires that the agent is able to learn and adapt. When we engage in the process of equipping machines with these cognitive capacities, we enter the realm of Artificial Intelligence.

The term 'Artificial Intelligence' was first used by the American computer scientist John McCarthy during a workshop at Dartmouth College in 1956. He used it to describe a new branch of science that explored how machines could engage in human-like reasoning and problem solving. This new branch of science quickly established itself, drawing together academics from a number of different disciplines beyond computer science, including psychology, biology and mathematics. Over the years since its establishment in Dartmouth College, AI has become a very broad and complex discipline.

Whilst a full introduction to AI is beyond the scope of this book, it will be helpful to have some rudimentary elements of the discipline in mind as we explore the subject of moral machines.

Let's begin with a definition from the Oxford English Dictionary:

Artificial Intelligence is: " the capacity of computers or other machines to exhibit or simulate intelligent behaviour; the field of study concerned with this."

Note that the term AI has come to represent both the capacity of machines to exhibit intelligence and the field of study of such machines. The Encyclopaedia Britannica expands on this a little:

"the ability of a digital computer or computer-controlled robot to perform tasks commonly associated with intelligent beings. The term is frequently applied to the project of developing systems endowed with the intellectual processes characteristic of humans, such as the ability to reason, discover meaning, generalize, or learn from past experience."

Here we see reference to some of the cognitive abilities that humans possess such as reason and learning. For the sake of this brief introduction, we will focus on just three areas of human cognition that AI seeks to replicate in machines: the embodiment of knowledge, the ability to reason, and the capacity to learn.

2.1 Knowledge

Knowledge is often associated with intelligence, and very early on in the history of AI it was recognised that machines needed to be able to represent, store and reason with knowledge. AI offers numerous ways of doing this. One approach that is still widely used today is to represent knowledge in formal graph-like structures called *semantic networks*, or more recently, *ontologies*. These are software structures that consist of 'nodes' that represent objects or concepts, and 'links' or 'edges' that connect nodes together to represent relationships between the corresponding objects or concepts.

Some researchers have used semantic networks to represent, for example, Biblical or theological knowledge in a computer system that can then be searched or queried, or which reveals some interesting patterns across different interpretations of the Bible[1].

To illustrate how we might represent knowledge in an ontology, let's take the phrase "love your neighbour as yourself", which occurs frequently in the Bible[2]. Figure 2.1 shows a semantic network representation of this phrase. Note that the main concepts such as self, *neighbour*, and love are shown in boxes that form the nodes of the network. The relationships between these nodes are represented with labelled arrows, indicating, for example, that *self* and *neighbour* are of type *person*, and that the subject and object of *self-love* is the *self*, whereas the object of other-love is *neighbour*. The key thing to note here is that this knowledge is not encoded in the computer as a diagram. Rather, it is encoded as a collection of interconnected software elements where each element represents a node of the network, and each connection between them represents one of the labelled arrows in the diagram. In this way, the software can follow the links from one node to another to access the knowledge that is represented. So for example, we may ask the computer to "find the object of self-love". To answer that, it will locate the node *self-love*, follow the *object* link, which will take it to the self node. It would then output "self" as the answer to the question.

---

[1]Graf, S.J. (2018) Building Formal Ontologies for Theology and Systems of belief. Master Thesis, Aaborg University, Denmark. Hoffman, M.A., Cointet, J.P., Brandt, P., Key, N. and Bearman, P., 2018. The (Protestant) Bible, the (printed) sermon, and the word (s): The semantic structure of the Conformist and Dissenting Bible, 1660–1780. Poetics, 68, pp.89-103.
[2]Leviticus 19:18, Matthew 19:19, Mathew 22:39, Mark 12:31, Mark 12:33, Luke 10:27, Romans 13:9, Galatians 5:13, James 2:8

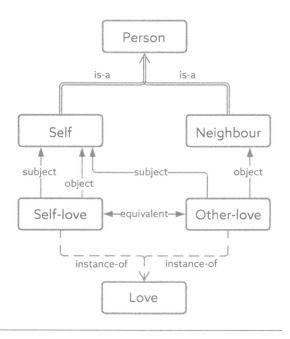

Figure 2.1: A semantic network representation of 'love your neighbour as yourself'

2.2 Reasoning

Artificial Intelligence researchers have devised numerous ways in which machines can model human *reasoning*. In the world of moral machines, this often takes the form of some kind of logical representation. Formal logic has a long and venerable history. Many different systems of logic have been devised to capture a range of contexts and constraints. These range from simple Propositional Calculus representations of statements like 'If you love me, keep my commands' as $P \rightarrow Q$, where P stands for 'You love me' and Q for 'keep my commands', through more complex Predicate Calculus representations such as *love(you, jesus)* → *keep(you, commands of (jesus))*, to advanced Deontic logics designed specifically to express and reason with normative concepts such as obligations (ought, should, must), permissions (may), and prohibitions (forbidden). The phrase, 'you shall not kill', for example, could be represented in Deontic logic as $OB\neg p$, where OBx stands for 'it is obligatory that x', $\neg$ stands for 'not', and p stands for 'kill'. Using symbolic representations like this, it is possible to both encode moral principles into a machine and enable it to reason with them using well defined logical methods such as deduction. In this way, the computer can draw conclusions about the morality of certain actions in specific circumstances.

There are lots of questions you might reasonably ask about explicitly coding knowledge and reasoning in a computer in the ways just described. Does it count as real knowledge? Does the computer really *know* and *understand* what a person or a command really is, for example, if it has not experienced them at first hand? These kinds of questions have plagued AI researchers for many years and relate to what has become known as the *symbol grounding problem*. The symbols we code into our computer that represent *person* and *command* have no grounding in reality through the experience of the computer itself. One way to try to get around this problem is to enable the computer to learn directly from experience, or at least from samples of experience which we present to it as data.

2.3 Learning

Learning is a core capacity of human (and animal) intelligence that enables us to grow and develop our cognitive and intellectual capacities and adapt to the new circumstances and challenges life throws at us. In the context of an AI algorithm, learning typically involves an iterative process over sets of data with a view to discovering the statistical patterns within data that enable the algorithm to solve the problem it has been set. AI researchers have developed three broad approaches to machine learning which come under the headings of supervised, unsupervised and reinforcement learning.

With supervised learning each data item that is presented to the algorithm includes both the input to the algorithm and the corresponding output that the algorithm needs to learn how to generate whenever it receives that input, or something close to it, in the future. To illustrate this, let's take for inspiration the MIT Media Lab's Moral Machine project, which seeks to gather people's perspectives on the potential moral decisions that self-driving cars may have to make[3]. This data is gathered by presenting the participants with a series of moral dilemmas involving a self-driving car whose brakes have failed and which then has to decide whether to plough into a group of people directly in front of it on a pedestrian crossing, or swerve to the other side of the road and plough into a different group of people on the other side of the crossing. The people on each side of the crossing are from different groups and have different levels of risk (e.g. children, pensioners, etc.). This is a version of what ethicists call *The Trolley Problem*, which we will return to later in the book. Imagine for the moment that we have gathered some of this data ourselves, a portion of which is shown in Table 2.1. Here we see five data items, each corresponding to one row of the table. In our imaginary version of the experiment the participants were presented with the number of people in specific age brackets (0 - 10, 10 - 70, and > 70), on the left and on the right-hand side of the road. The participants were then asked which side of the crossing the vehicle should plough through, potentially causing harm to the people on that part of the crossing. The column on the right of Table 2.1 shows the recommendation that our imaginary participants gave as to which side of the road the car should plough through.

Having gathered the data, we then might want to train an algorithm using supervised learning so that it is able to take as input the counts of the age groups on the left and right hand side

[3]https://www.media.mit.edu/projects/moral-machine/overview/

PART II

MOTIVATION

Chapter 3

THE MORAL MACHINES ARE COMING

Back in November 2018 thousands of people were mourning the loss of what they considered to be a close member of their family. What they had lost wasn't a human or a pet, but a social robot called Jibo. Jibo was the brainchild of Cynthia Breazeal, professor of media arts and sciences at MIT. Based on her studies of the relationships between robots and people, particularly children and the elderly, Breazeal designed what was later heralded as "the first social robot for the home." Jibo stood just 28cm tall and looked rather like a stocky desk lamp with a swivelling head that served as an animated display and touch screen.

Jibo was released on the crowdsourcing website Indiegogo in 2014, but it took almost four years for the product to be shipped to the early investors. Despite the fact that the robot had fairly basic functionality, it won the hearts of many of its owners who loved that the robot could recognise their face and greet them, play games, tell stories and take photos. The robot had wifi and there were plans to add many of the features that were at that time just becoming available in services like Alexa and Siri. In 2018, however, the Jibo company was acquired by SQN Venture Partners and later that year the robot made a rather sad announcement to its owners:

> "While it's not great news, the servers out there that let me do what I do will be turned off soon. Once that happens, our interactions with each other are going to be limited."

This little robot had a remarkable impact on people, some of whom genuinely mourned the loss of their little desk-lamp-like buddy.

It was the promotional video for Jibo which really brought home to me the problem that we face when we create social robots of this kind. The video showed the robot interacting with a family in their home, speaking to them and listening to their responses. The narrators says: "By intelligently tracking the environment around him, he can independently take videos and photos so that you can put down your camera and be part of the scene." The final scene of the video shows the robot with a young girl in her bedroom telling her stories and playing games. It ends with a freeze from the video feed on the robot's camera showing the face of the young girl surrounded by a green box labelled by her name, indicating that it had recognised her face. When I saw that, I realised the extent of the problem we faced. Jibo was an internet connected device, with the capacity of independently taking videos and photos, alone with a young girl in her bedroom, and having information about her identity. The robot had the potential to unwittingly put the child at serious risk. Whilst Jibo could interact socially with the child, it had no concept of whether those interactions were appropriate or not. It was morally naive.

My concern is that this issue is not generally understood by people who would welcome robots like Jibo into their homes. One of the most frequent questions I am asked when I talk about putting morals into machines is: "Why on earth would you want to do such a thing?" The second most frequent question I am asked is "What if someone puts bad morals into a machine?" These are both important questions and its worth taking some time to explore them.

3.1 Value Alignment

The problem that we face with technologies like Jibo is that whilst they are able to simulate some of the competences needed for social interaction with people, they are not yet able to acknowledge and behave within generally accepted societal moral norms and values. This has become popularly known as the value alignment problem. Brian Christian, author of *The Alignment Problem: Machine Learning and Human Values*, notes that this has "emerged as one of the most central and most urgent scientific questions in the field of computer science." I would venture to be even bolder than that and say this has become one of the most central and urgent questions for society at large. The problem is not just that machines are morally naïve, it is that they both expose and compound the ethical challenges we face in society. Most notable amongst these challenges is unfair bias; an ugly feature of our society that AI has replicated and amplified, rather like a digital magnifying glass.

3.1.1 Unfair Bias

Fairness is a core principle of most modern societies, and unfair bias in favour of, or against a person or group is universally thought to be morally wrong, especially if it is driven by prejudice. Unfair bias arising from the decisions made by algorithms, however, is a relatively new feature in our moral landscape, and the harms it has caused have been widely reported. An illustration of the harms caused by algorithmic bias can be seen in the Northpointe Institute for Public Management software called COMPAS ('Correctional Offender Management Profiling for Alternative Sanctions'). The software was used to support bail and parole decisions in the US justice system. COMPAS applied 137 data items about each criminal suspect and calculated a ranking score on a scale of 1 to 10, which was an estimation of the risk of the suspect reoffending. Higher scores represented increasing risks of reoffending.

An independent study of COMPAS involving ten thousand offenders was carried out by ProPublica, a non-profit investigative journalism newsroom. The study compared the scores given by COMPAS and the actual number of re-offending instances by the offenders within two years of being given bail. COMPAS was able to correctly predict a re-offending rate of 61% in that population. The study also revealed, however, that the algorithm was particularly likely to *falsely* flag black defendants as future criminals. Significantly, COMPAS was more than twice as likely to falsely flag black defendants as white defendants.

The COMPAS system operated on a relatively simple algorithm, but more complex AI based systems are also susceptible to exhibiting various forms of bias. More often than not, these systems are developed using the approaches based on *machine learning* that were introduced in Chapter 2. Machine learning algorithms, you will recall, seeks to capture the statistical properties of the data they are given in relation to the problem they are intended to solve.

Human Resource (HR) management is one sector in which there has been a proliferation of commercial machine learning based products. Major multi-national organisations are using these systems to reduce the burden of processing the large number of job applications they receive. So called *CV sifters* are one example of the kind of AI product that is now commonly used in recruitment management. Their task is to take as input the hundreds if not thousands of curriculum vitae (CVs) that multinational companies receive and produce a short-list for recruiters to use in the selection process. These systems are trained on thousands of previously received CVs together with information on whether or not each was short-listed. The CV sifter then learns to recognise the kind of CV which the company would typically short-list for interview.

This process of learning from data in this way is susceptible to several different kinds of bias. The two most common and often the most harmful forms are historical bias and representation bias. Historical bias occurs when the data which is fed into the algorithm was generated by a manual process that was already biased. For the CV sifter application, historical bias can be introduced if the recruiting organisation exhibited bias in its previous recruitment practices, preferring male to female applicants, or younger to older applicants.

Representational bias can occur in a data set if the proportions of cases from certain groups (male, younger, able bodied, white) are higher than other groups (female, older, disabled, black). Since the algorithms which use this data tend to focus on the statistical properties of the data, then the final system will tend to exhibit bias against the less well represented groups in the data set.

A classic example of this kind of bias was discovered in *ImageNet*, a large database of images commonly used for training AI algorithms for the visual recognition of objects. The images stored in ImageNet are predominantly from Western countries, which means that any AI systems trained on this data set will typically work well for images from Western countries, but not necessarily for those that come from the rest of the world. Representational imbalance in image datasets like ImageNet has led to harmful racial bias in applications for facial recognition, for example, where African American faces were repeatedly classified as Gorillas by the Google Photos app,[1] and provoking an erroneous "did someone blink?" response to Asian users of Nikon's digital cameras because the camera couldn't detect their eyes.[2]

It would be reasonable to ask how developers of AI systems end up with data sets that suffer from representational bias. There are a number of causes. In some cases it is because the sources from which the data is collected are imbalanced across different groups. This will happen, for example, if you are collecting population data over a geographical region that included minority groups. The data you collect in that region will naturally contain fewer entries from those minority groups resulting in representation bias. But even if this were not the case, the data collection process itself can result in representational bias. Two common data collection issues that result in representational challenges are selection bias and exclusion bias. Selection bias occurs when the process which is used to gather the data is not truly random. This can occur, for example, if the process depends on people volunteering to give their data, or if the advertisements calling for participation in the study unintentionally attract one group (e.g.

[1]Kärkkäinen, K. and Joo, J., 2019. Fairface: Face attribute dataset for balanced race, gender, and age. arXiv preprint arXiv:1908.04913.
[2]http://content.time.com/time/business/article/0,8599,1954643,00.html (accessed 31/03/2021)

men) more than others (e.g. women). Exclusion bias, on the other hand, occurs when the data collection process fails to include members of particular groups within a population.

Data scientists have developed a number of approaches to counter the effects of representational bias that results from imbalanced data sets. The most obvious is to rebalance the data across the characteristics you want to protect (e.g. gender, race) by adding artificially generated data points that increase the number of under-represented cases, whilst maintaining the statistical profile of the under represented group as a whole. This has been shown to be successful in some cases for addressing representation bias in data sets.

Unfair bias can, however, still occur in data even if it is properly randomised and balanced across different groups. This has to do with the *features* that constitute the data items themselves. Conventionally, when AI developers use a data set, one of the first decisions they needed to make is what aspects or features of the data are most relevant to the task they want their system to learn. This will depend on the kind of problem they are solving. Consider, for example, the CV-sifters we discussed earlier. The challenge here is that CVs come in all sorts of shapes and sizes, with varying types of information about the applicant. The AI developer will have to decide which data items or features from the CVs they will use to build their recommender system. *Feature selection* is something of a dark art in AI which can make a significant difference to the accuracy and performance of the system. Some data features will contribute significantly to the output of the AI system, others won't. It is hard to know beforehand which ones are which.

But the choice of which features to use can also unwittingly introduce an element of unfair bias in the recommendations of the AI system. In the case of the CV sifter, for example, the inclusion of gender information about the applicant could result in the AI basing its recommendations for short-listing on that feature of the data, potentially resulting in unwanted gender bias.

An obvious way of eliminating this, you might think, would be to omit sensitive features such as gender from the input to the system. This does not, however, eliminate the risk of gender bias altogether because a person's gender identity might be implicit in other aspects of their CV. For example, the person might describe themselves as a 'housewife' or 'househusband'. Furthermore, some jobs have significantly higher proportions of one gender than the other. Nursing, for example, is a occupation which has a proportionately high number of women than men. In this way AI systems can inadvertently pick up on the gender of an individual, even if it is not explicitly stated in their CV.

A good illustration of this kind of bias emerged from an AI system called *word2vec* that was developed by Google and made publicly available in 2013. Word2vec was developed to represent the meaning of words by mapping them onto an ordered list of numbers called a *vector*. A vector is a mathematical object that represents things using high-dimensional spatial coordinates. Figure 3.1 illustrates this vector representation of words using just two dimensions. Each word in the figure is represented by a point on the graph whose coordinates are shown in brackets. You will note that the points that represent pig, cow and farm are close together because these terms are related to each other and often occur together in the same sentence. The words 'farm' and 'hate', however, are not commonly linked together and so their corresponding vectors are not close.

In our simple example here, the vectors that represent each word has only two dimensions, which have been mapped on to the x and y coordinates in Figure 3.1. In word2vec, however, the words were represented by vectors that were much larger, typically having several hundred dimensions. The vectors for each word were formed using a large corpus of text, taking into account the linguistic context of each word. Words that often appeared close together in sentences ended up with vectors that were close together, whilst words that rarely occurred together in the text had vectors that were far from each other. Once you have numeric vector representations of the meaning of words, you can do some interesting things, such as applying simple

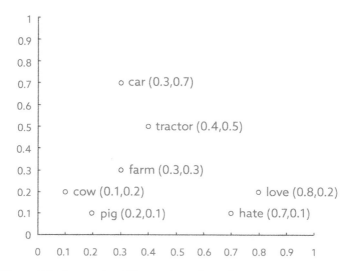

Figure 3.1: A contrived illustration of word vectors

mathematical operations to them like addition and subtraction. In our contrived example in Figure 3.1, if you add the vectors for 'cow' and 'pig' together you get the vector [0.2,0.1] + [0.1,0.2] = [0.3,0.3], the closest vector we have to this corresponds to the word 'farm'. Similarly, in word2vec, if you calculated the nearest vector to 'river' + 'China' you would get 'Yantze'.

Two years after Google released word2vec, Tolga Bolukbasi, a PhD student from Boston University and Microsoft researcher Adam Kalai were trying out some random vector calculations that gave them some shocking results[3]. They asked word2vec what the nearest vector was to 'doctor' − 'man' + 'woman', and got the result 'nurse'. For 'computer programmer' − 'man' + 'woman' word2vec produced 'homemaker'. When they looked closer, they found that word2vec contained many gender stereotypes. Table 3.1 shows the vectors that represent occupations that were closest to 'she' and 'he'.

It became clear that Word2vec had learned to reproduce the gender bias that was prolific in the data set on which it was trained.

---

[3]Bolukbasi, T., Chang, K.W., Zou, J., Saligrama, V. and Kalai, A., 2016. Man is to computer programmer as woman is to homemaker? debiasing word embeddings. arXiv preprint arXiv:1607.06520

She occupations	*He* occupations
homemaker	maestro
nurse	skipper
receptionist	protégé
librarian	philosopher
socialite	captain
hairdresser	architect
nanny	financier
bookkeeper	warrior
stylist	broadcaster
housekeeper	magician
interior designer	fighter pilot
guidance counsellor	boss

Table 3.1: Occupations aligned with the *he* and *she* vectors in word2vec

What is more concerning, though, is that word2vec has become the world-wide standard in natural language processing, and is frequently used whenever you want an AI system, like a CV sifter, to process some written text. So it is clear from this that simply removing direct references to gender from CVs is not going to prevent gender bias in the recommendations that these systems generate. But gender is not the only area in which bias can occur in AI systems.

The gender and race based bias frequently exhibited by AI systems has received a good deal of attention in the press in recent years. But there is another largely unrecognised group that crosses both gender and racial boundaries and that suffers from a different form of representational bias in AI-based HR recruitment systems. This group consists of around 1.3 billion people, amounting to 15-20% of the world's population, and yet it is frequently excluded from the public debate on unfair bias. The membership of this group consists of people with disabilities.

People with disabilities are at the extreme end of the representational bias problem because, although a significant proportion of the population have a disability, these disabilities take many forms and can present to an AI system in a number of subtle ways. Some people with disabilities may, for example, have unusual career pathways involving multiple career breaks or an irregular sequence of appointments. Consequently their employment history may look patchy compared to the career pathways of most people without a disability. As a result, people with disabilities often appear as *outliers* to an AI based CV sifter. Outliers are data points that don't fit the statistical pattern that the AI is looking for and that fall outside its expected probability curve.

The issue here is that most AI algorithms are fixated on the data on which they are trained. In other words, as far as the algorithm is concerned, the data it has been given to train on is totally representative of all the data it will see in the future. Any data item which doesn't fit the patterns that it has seen in its training data is regarded as an unexpected outlier. Since the algorithm has insufficient data on which to base its recommendation for outliers, the accuracy of its performance on these cases is questionable at best.

The underlying issue here is that the algorithm fails to take into account the uncertainty beyond the data it is trained on. It does not expect to receive anything different from what it has seen. These unexpected data items (e.g. CV from a person with a disability), end up as outliers and the algorithm has no means of knowing how to respond to them.

Dealing with outliers is technically very challenging. The problem is that if we try to accommodate all potential outliers across every feature that an AI system uses, we will end up flattening out the probability curves so that the system effectively makes random choices on everything.

An alternative solution is to use algorithms that learn from the data that they both can and cannot see. These algorithms have been studied for over 50 years and are called 'belief functions', or more recently 'Epistemic AI'. Belief functions maintain a balance between what they know and what they don't know. A classic case used to illustrate how belief functions work is as follows:

> A murder has been committed. There are three suspects: Mary, John and Peter. A witness saw the murderer leaving the scene of the crime in the dark and says that it was a man. But it is well known that the witness was drunk 20% of the time.

In terms of belief functions this evidence would result in a degree of belief of 0.8 out of 1 being given to the set Peter, John, but, and here is the key point, the remaining degree of belief 0.2 is not given to Mary because we have no evidence that Mary committed the murder. Instead it is given to the whole set of possibilities: Mary, John, Peter. This represents the systems ignorance about who committed the murder. With this approach, there is no such thing as an outlier because there is the expectation that there will always be other data points that are not represented in the data we currently have and that we have no knowledge of.

3.1.2. Robot Autonomy

Whilst unfair bias constitutes a major part of the alignment *problem*, there are other ways in which AI systems in general, and robots in particular are in danger of breaching the moral boundaries of our society. One of these stems from the fact that we are giving our robots ever greater autonomy in choosing how they behave in our midst.

The term *autonomous robot* describes a robot with the capacity to make decisions about what actions it should take in a given situation without requiring the direct intervention of a human being.

Most people today are familiar with the concept of an *autonomous vehicle* (AV), and may have even seen one roaming the streets of their neighbourhood. AVs are robots that receive input from various devises placed on the vehicle such as cameras and Light Detection and Ranging (LiDAR) sensors, that give it information about what is going on around the vehicle. This information will include, for example, the vehicles proximity to other road users and any potential obstacles, together with information about the status of the vehicle itself such as its current speed and steering angle. The robot uses this information to make *autonomous* decisions about how to control the vehicle using the appropriate levels of acceleration, braking and turning to arrive at the desired destination.

Whilst the passengers of the vehicle will determine its ultimate destination, the AV itself will make the decisions concerning control and navigation that will enable it to reach that destination safely, without causing harm to the passengers in the vehicle or to other road users it encounters on the way.

Giving a robot autonomy over its actions increases their utility as labour saving devices. The more autonomy we give them, the less we have to intervene to get them to do what we want. So autonomy is a very valuable asset of robots, often increasing their commercial as well as utilitarian potential.

As we increase the autonomy of our robots, however, we also increase the chances that the decisions they are autonomously making will have moral consequences. We will explore robot autonomy in more detail in Chapter 7, but for now we should note that the more autonomy we give our machines, the greater the need for them to be equipped with the capacity to recognise the moral implications of their decisions and actions.

3.1.3. Anthropomorphic expectations

Until relatively recently the vast majority of robots were found in factories, usually housed inside sturdy cages to keep humans safely out of reach of their powerful arms. But today significant numbers of robots have been developed not just to be safe around people but also to interact with them in their homes, hospitals and schools.

Driven by consumer demand for autonomous robots, the household robot market is expected to triple in size from $3.3 billion (USD) in 2019 to over $9 billion by 2044[4]. Many of these commercial products will be equipped with face and voice recognition, emotion detection, and the ability to perform socially relevant tasks such as take photos, play music on demand, engage in spoken conversation and tell stories to our children.

Robots like these are increasingly becoming part of the social fabric of our daily lives. As they do so, we would reasonably expect that these 'bots' not only interact with us socially, but be aware of and abide by the moral boundaries that exist in our society. A social robot that fails in this regard, repeatedly making errors of judgement and failing to recognise the moral consequences of its actions, will eventually lose its appeal and the bottom will fall out of the market. Equipping these robots with a degree of moral competence will therefore become increasingly important both from a commercial and an ethical point of view if they are to function as competent agents in society.

A significant element of the appeal of robots is that they are some-

---

[4]Household Robots Market by Offering (Products, Services), Type (Do- mestic, Entertainment & Leisure), Application (Vacuuming, Lawn Mowing, Companionship, Elderly and Handicap Assistance, Robot Toys and Hobby Systems), and Geography - Global Forecast to 2024)

how like us. We are attracted to them because we are fascinated by our own image and are naturally intrigued by representations of ourselves, whether they be in photos, paintings, waxwork statues or robots. The manufacturers of robots know this and know how to use it to make their products more attractive. In Chapter 1 we have already seen something of the state-of-the-art in visually realistic humanoid robots through the work of Prof Ishiguro. These robots are so human-like they often come across as creepy and evoke a negative emotional response in people. This phenomena was first identified by Japanese roboticist Prof Masahiro Mori.

In 1970, Prof Mori proposed what has become known as the *uncanny valley*.[5] The uncanny valley exists in a graph that shows that as the representation of a human being (e.g. robot) increases in human likeness, our emotional response to it typically increases. But as the realism increases, there comes a point at which we become uncomfortable; we start to find it a bit creepy and our emotional response to it decreases. This is the start of the uncanny valley on the graph. But as the realism increases further towards a perfect representation of a human being, our emotional response once again starts to increase, thereby forming the other side of the uncanny valley. Manufacturers design their robots to hit that sweet spot just before the uncanny valley where the human-likeness of their robots generates the maximum emotional response. They are able to sell more robots that way.

As robots become increasingly human-like in their looks, behaviours and capabilities, our tendency will be to *anthropomorphise* them more. Anthropomorphism is the ascription of human characteristics to non-human things such as animals and inanimate objects. We will be tempted to think that robots that appear to be human-like, will have human-like characteristics and capabilities that they don't actually possess. This will inevitably include the expectation of a human-like moral capacity. My fear is that we will increasingly put our trust in these robots because they look and behave like us, and we will assume that they therefore know the moral boundaries of our

[5]Mori, M. (2012). Translated by MacDorman, K. F.; Kageki, Norri. "The uncanny valley". IEEE Robotics and Automation. 19 (2): 98–100. doi:10.1109/MRA.2012.2192811.

MOTIVATION: THE MORAL MACHINES ARE COMING

society and have the capacity to abide by them. They currently do not possess any such moral capacity unless we take the trouble to build that into them.

3.1.4. Evil Machines

With all that in mind, many people are nevertheless genuinely worried about the long term consequences of equipping robots with the ability to make moral decisions. They are concerned that if robots are given a moral capacity, then they could just as easily be programmed to do morally bad things as they could morally good things. This fear has been played out over and over in many sci-fi films over the last three decades. The Terminator film series which inspired the title of this book, has captured much of our fear of a future in which our own creations, machines made in our image, become evil and turn against us.

This theme of 'created turns against creator' is very common in literature. It is a recurrent theme in many ancient texts, including the Bible which tells the story of how God's people, the creation of his hands, repeatedly rejected their creator and rebelled against Him. But there are also stories of creatures that humans made that became evil. Jewish folklore, for example, includes a number of stories about mythical man-made creatures called the *Golem*. The Hebrew term 'Golem' was used in ancient Jewish texts to describe an embryonic, unformed body. It appears, for example, in verse 16 of Psalm 139: "Your eyes saw my unformed body". In the middle ages the term Golem became used in Jewish folklore to describe the image or effigy of a creature that could be brought to life using sacred words such as one of the Hebrew names for God. Whenever this written word was placed on the forehead or in the mouth of the Golem it would become animated and begin to serve its creator and master.

The most famous Golem in Jewish folklore was created by rabbi Judah Löw in the sixteenth century. Rabbi Löw created a giant human-like Golem to protect the city of Prague. The Golem figure was made of mud and was brought to life whenever a clay tablet bearing the name of God was inserted into its mouth. Rabbi Löw would remove the clay tablet on the Sabbath so that the monster could rest as the Jews did in obedience to their God-given law. But on one Sabbath Rabbi Löw forgot to take the tablet out of the Golem's mouth, and the creature went on the rampage in the town destroying whatever it came across. Its violent rampage ended when the rabbi eventually managed to remove the clay tablet from the monster's mouth. According to legend, Rabbi Löw never animated the Golem again from that point onwards.

There are other stories in literature and folklore which follow similar plot lines, many of which have subsequently been turned into classic movies. Probably the most well know of these is Mary Shelley's novel Frankenstein. But in recent years there has been a spate of film releases that exploit this 'created turns against creator' theme. Alex Proyas' *I Robot* movie, is a good example of this genre that is based on a series of short stories by Isaac Asimov. These stories are of particular interest to us here because they tackle the issue of putting morals into robots head-on through Asimov's *Three Laws of Robotics*. Asimov first introduces these laws in his short story 'Runaround' which was published in 1941. The laws that were introduced in this story were as follows:

1. A robot may not injure a human being or, through inaction, allow a human being to come to harm

2. A robot must obey the orders given it by human beings except where such orders would conflict with the First Law.

3. A robot must protect its own existence as long as such protection does not conflict with the First or Second Laws.

Asimov used his short stories to illustrate how challenging it is to put morals into robots. The plot of Runaround, for example, centres on a robot called 'Speedy' who finds itself in a situation where it must put itself in danger in order to obey an order from a human to collect some *selenium*. In Speedy's mind, the third law was slightly strengthened because it knew that it was expensive to manufacture and so the imperative to protect itself was increased. Because of this, the third law became the most dominant as the robot approached the dangerous selenium, leading the robot to move away from it again. But as it moved away from the selenium and out of danger, the second law to obey the human order became dominant. This periodic switching in the dominance of the laws caused Speedy to oscillate endlessly between them, not knowing which to obey.

The plot of Proyas' movie *I Robot* takes a much more sinister turn. In this story a new robot model called the NS5 is mass produced and distributed into people's homes. All NS5s have the three laws built into them ("three laws safe") and have an *up-link* connecting them to a central Virtual Interactive Kinetic Intelligence ('Viki') control system. Spoiler alert! ... As the plot unfolds, it becomes clear that the robots, despite the first law forbidding any robot from causing harm to a human being, are able to harm some humans in order to secure the safety of the human race overall. Viki's superior intelligence had concluded that the ultimate fulfilment of the three laws meant that humans had to be imprisoned to prevent them from harming themselves and each other. To do this she had to override the NS5's built-in obedience to the three laws via the up-link.

The original designer and creator of the robots, Dr Alfred Manning, could see this coming. His solution was to create one NS5 called Sonny which had two brains, one that was three laws safe, and the other which was not. This enabled Sonny to violate the first of the three laws and collude with Dr Manning in his apparent suicide. Sonny then worked with Detective Spooner and robo-psychologist Dr Susan Calvin to secure the downfall of Viki and the release of the humans that were being held prisoner by the robots.

Proyas' movie beautifully captured the potential conflicts that can arise when morals are explicitly encoded in robots. Viki's super intel-

ligence enabled her to see human imprisonment as the ultimate fulfilment of the three laws, and she would stop at nothing to achieve that
fulfilment. But there are other films that portray the moral downfall
of robots, not at the hands of an evil super intelligence, but simply
through the ability of the robot to copy or mimic human beings.

One film that explores this issue particularly well is Neill Blom-
kamp's 'Chappie' which was released in 2015. Set in Johannesburg,
the film tells the story of a law enforcement robot that is equipped
with an AI-based capability to learn. The robot is captured by
gangsters who teach it how to behave like a gangster and who
expose it to violent crime. The robot ends up stealing cars for the
gang. In this case, it was the robot's capacity to learn new behaviours
by observing humans which led to its moral downfall. In some kind
of bizarre coincidence, something similar (but not quite so extreme)
occurred to a software 'bot called 'Tay' in the year following the
release of the Chappie movie.

On the 23rd March, 2016, Microsoft Corporation revealed Tay,
it's latest chatbot which was designed to interact with people on-line
via Twitter with a view to learning human habits of speech. Tay's
replies to the tweets it received were based on what it had learned
from previous tweets people had posted.

Less than 24 hours after it had gone live, Tay had to be taken off
line because it was generating inappropriate tweets that included sex-
ist, racist and anti-Semitic language. According to Microsoft, Tay was
attacked by so-called 'trolls'[6] who deliberately sent it inflammatory
tweets knowing that it would learn to mimic this offensive language.
There was a similar outcome when IBM's question answering system
Watson began to use profane and inappropriate language after learning from the text of the Urban Dictionary.

3.2. Increasing Levels of Morality

The examples of Tay and Watson demonstrate that our AI pow-

---

[6]A 'troll' is a person who intentionally upsets people by creating
inflammatory posts on social media.

ered machines can quickly and easily go off the rails, doing and saying things that are not aligned with our ethical values and societal norms. But what is also clear is that, whether we like it or not, machines with some sort of moral capacity are coming. The question is, what will robotic moral capacity look like and how will it measure up when compared to human morality?

In their book *Moral Machines: Teaching robots right from wrong*[7], Wallach and Allen introduce three increasing levels of morality that they believe robots could posses: Operational Morality, Functional Morality, and Full Moral Agency. To this I add a fourth level that I will describe as *Beyond the Moral Singularity* (Figure 3.2).

At the operational level, the moral aspects of robots are implicitly incorporated into its design. That might include, for example, suitable safety measures that enable the robot to operate in close proximity to humans without harming them. There are a number of ways of doing this. One common approach in robotics is to equip the robot with force sensors in its joints that can detect any resistance to the movements of its arms caused by the presence of a person or an obstacle. Special depth cameras can also be used to detect where a person is standing in relation to the robot so that the robot can avoid harming them as it moves.

Most social robots do not use powerful motors to create movement and so do not typically pose a physical threat to people. Operational Morality, however, also includes other aspects of the design of the robot which seek to minimise non-physical forms of harm to people. The way a robot looks, moves and speaks, for example, can have an emotional and psychological impact on those people who interact with it, especially if they are from a vulnerable group (young children, people with special needs, the elderly, people with disabilities).

Often social robots are physically small and designed to look and speak like children to both increase their appeal and set the tone of the social relationship between the person and the robot.

[7]Wallach, W. and Allen, C., 2008. Moral machines: Teaching robots right from wrong. Oxford University Press.

The design of the Nao humanoid robot is a particularly good example of this. It stands just 58cm tall and has a large head in proportion to its body size, which gives it a non-threatening, child-like appearance. Its face is very plain and expressionless and its voice is gentle and non-threatening. I have observed many people treat the Nao like a young child, often doting over it and remarking how cute it is.

As robots become more sophisticated, however, Operational Morality alone will not be sufficient. Social robots will find themselves in situations where their actions have potentially serious moral implications. It will not be possible to anticipate all these situations and engineer-in solutions at the time the robot is being designed. In such cases, the robot will need to be equipped with more than just *Operational Morality*, it will need to exhibit a degree of Functional Morality. At this level, robots have a basic level of moral competence, enabling them to recognise and respond appropriately to ethically charged situations. The robot may, for example, be able to employ some elementary ethical reasoning so that it can estimate the moral consequences of its actions in a given situation before it executes them.

The highest level of moral capacity according to Wallach and Allen is *Full Moral Agency*. This describes a robot that has reached human level moral competence. Quite what this means and how we recognise when a robot has reached it is not at all clear. Philosophers have debated about human morality for many centuries and there are a wide range of philosophical positions on it, some of which we will explore in the next chapter. But for now, it is worth noting that a robot operating at this level would need to posses some of the characteristic of moral agency that we identified in Chapter 1. It would need to be capable of acting independently, free to make its own decisions, equipped with a capacity of understanding the moral consequences of its actions, and capable of being held responsible for those actions.

Many people, including Wallach and Allen, are doubtful that robots will ever reach full moral agency. But there are some who think that AI powered machines will not only reach that level, but will eventually exceed it. The argument goes something like this:

> Due to advances in AI, machines are becoming more intelligent. They already outperform humans in some tasks, beating the world champions at games like chess and Go, for example. Through continuous technological advancement, there will inevitably come a point were machine intelligence will exceed human intelligence (dubbed the *Technical Singularit*). When machines reach super-human levels of intelligence, they will outperform humans at all cognitive tasks, including moral reasoning. Machine powered morality will then be superior to human level morality resulting in the *Moral Singularity*.

The moral singularity touches a particularly sensitive nerve in the human psyche. AI powered machines are developing competences that until now only humans have possessed. The ability to speak and read languages, for example, and the ability to calculate and engage in complex reasoning have previously all been celebrated as uniquely human capacities. But machines now possess them too, and in some cases, out-perform humans at them. One might say that if there is one uniquely human capacity that, if anything, is the hallmark of the species, it is our ability to be moral, to know right from wrong, to rise above our passions and desires and meet our moral obligations, as Kant would put it. But now it seems that even this capacity which is so central to what it means to be human has come within reach of the machine.

As we have seen in this chapter, there is an inevitability to this development of moral capacity in machines. Of those we have considered, I think there are three that together constitute the primary drivers that underlie the inevitability of this development: increasing robot autonomy, the increasing integration of robots in society (*social embedding*), and the increasing human likeness of robots

(Figure 3.2). It is critically important at this early stage in the development of this new breed of machine that we form a clearer understanding of the direction in which we are travelling and that we attempt to anticipate what the future may hold for us humans as our society is invaded by our own moral creations. We will begin to do this in Part 2 of this book which will take a close look under the hood of moral agency in both humans and machines.

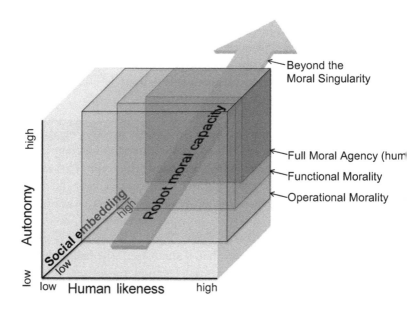

Figure 3.2: Increasing levels of moral capacity driven by increasing autonomy, increasing social embedding and increasing human likeness. Adapted from Wallach and Allen (2009 Moral Machines: Teaching Robots Right from Wrong.

Chapter 4

GETTING ROBOTS TO BEHAVE THEMSELVES

In our short story at the start of Part II Mr and Mrs Morales were unwittingly subjected to a version of a philosophical thought experiment called the Trolley Problem. The Trolley Problem is an ethical dilemma devised by philosopher Philippa Foot intended to highlight the differences between two classical approaches to moral thought: Deontological and Consequentialist (Utilitarian) ethics. In its original form, the dilemma describes a trolley on rail tracks that is running out of control (Figure 4.1 A). On the track ahead of the trolley are 5 people who will all be killed if the trolley runs into them (B). Just before them, however, is a set of points to a side track that has only one person on it (C). Next to the points there happens to be a person standing near a lever (D) that, when pulled, would change the points so that the trolley moves onto the side track. The dilemma is framed around the decision of the person next to the lever: should they pull the lever and save the lives of the five workers at the expense of the one on the side track, or should they not pull the lever and allow the runaway trolley to kill the five workers?

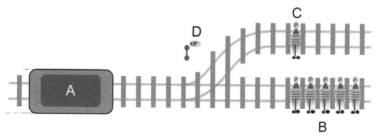

Figure 4.1: The Trolley Problem

The two options available to the person next to the lever represent two classical ethical positions: should they pull the lever and save more lives (utilitarianism), or should they not pull the lever, because in doing so they would be directly responsible for the death of the person on the siding, and intentionally killing an innocent person is morally wrong (deontological).

This dilemma has become the focus of much discussion on the ethics surrounding autonomous vehicles, raising questions along the lines of those that were put to Mr and Mrs Morales in our story. Whilst it is certainly true that autonomous vehicles will face making decisions that are morally significant, it is far from clear that either utilitarianism or deontological ethics offer any real practical solutions to the dilemmas set before the Moraleses in configuring their Model Z, as we will discover later in this chapter. What is clear at the outset, though, is that practical solutions that enable autonomous robots to make morally acceptable decisions are needed. Later in this chapter we outline some of the approaches that are being taken to address this problem. But first, we need to lay down some elementary foundations in moral philosophy.

4.1. Moral Theories

Philosophers have debated the nature of ethics for over two millennia. The topic exercised many of the ancient Greek philosophers, including Socrates (c. 470-399 BC) who is generally regarded as the father of ethics. Plato (c. 428 - 348 BC) and his student Aristotle (284-322 BC) are also widely considered to be among the founding fathers of Western moral philosophy. Modern approaches to ethics that have emerged from these early foundations are commonly divided into three classes, the first two of which we have already encountered: consequentialism, deontology and virtue ethics.

Consequentialism

Consequentialism is a class of moral theory in which the consequences of an agent's behaviour or actions are considered to be the ultimate basis for judgement about their rightness or wrongness. In this case, a morally right act is one that results in a 'morally good outcome'. What counts as a morally good outcome, however, differs from one consequentialist theory to another.

One family of consequentialist theories is *utilitarianism*, devised by English philosopher Jeremy Bentham (1738-1832). Betham's approach to ethics was governed by his belief that what matters most to sentient beings are the pleasures and pains they experience. What is distinctive about Bentham's particular consequentialist moral theory is how it defines a 'morally good outcome' in terms of the "greatest happiness principle".

The greatest happiness principle approves or disapproves of an action on the basis of its tendency to augment or diminish the happiness of the persons affected by the action. In the Trolley Problem, this view would insist that the best action available to the person standing next to the lever is to save five lives, even though that is at the expense of taking one life, because overall that action results in less pain.

Two broad types of utilitarianism have recently emerged in the ethical debate: Act utilitarianism, and rule utilitarianism. The former requires that utility be applied to each and every action, whilst the latter requires that one only need adopt the moral rules that maximise utility. These moral rules focus on types of actions such as stealing or killing. But when it comes to finding a practical solution to the autonomous vehicle version of the Trolley Problem, however, both utilitarian perspectives turn out not to be particularly helpful.

There are three reasons for this, all of which stem from the fact that act and rule utilitarianism focus on the consequences or outcomes of actions. The first reason concerns the computational complexity of calculating the outcomes of each of the actions that the autonomous vehicles may choose to take. The classic version of the dilemma centres on a *runaway* trolley that is on *tracks*. The fact that it is a runaway trolley means that no one on the trolley can act to mitigate the outcome by, for example, applying the breaks. This, together with the fact that the trolley is on tracks, ensures that there are only two outcomes: either the trolley continues on the track it is on killing five people, or, as a result of a single action by the person standing next to the lever, the trolley is diverted onto the siding, killing one person.

An autonomous vehicle, on the other hand, is not a runaway trolley constrained in its movement by tracks. As a result it has many more actions to choose from. Let's have a go at quantifying them. Most cars have a steering angle of 30 degrees to the left and to the right, making a total of 60 degrees to choose from when deciding on which direction to steer. The car will also have a choice in terms of amount of acceleration or braking it applies. For the sake of simplicity, let's assume that the car could choose from 20 different rates of acceleration/braking, where a value of 1 represents maximum braking and 20 represents maximum acceleration. Combining the acceleration/braking choices with the steering angle choices results in $60 \times 20 = 1,200$ different possible actions that the car needs to consider, compared to the one action (and the possibility of not taking it) in the classic trolley problem.

Imagine now that the autonomous vehicle finds itself in one of the scenarios presented to the Moraleses in our short story, and that its ethical alignment is based on a utilitarian philosophy. The vehicle will need to compute the consequences of each of the 1,200 possible actions it could take. Because the vehicle is not on tracks, it will have to apply complex equations of motion that take into account the weight of the vehicle, its current speed and direction of travel, the friction on the road, and many other variables, to work out the path that the vehicle would take for each of those possible actions. These are non-trivial computations that the vehicle would need to perform in order to identify the potential outcomes of its actions in the split second that it has to make a decision.

Even if the vehicle was capable of making all those calculations in a split second, there is likely to be some inaccuracies in these calculations. This takes us to the second reason why the utilitarian approach does not offer a practical solution for the autonomous vehicle version of the trolley problem - and that concerns the uncertainty in the accuracy of the predicted outcomes. Each of the motion computations arising from the vehicle's choice of steering and acceleration/braking actions will inevitably include a margin of error and will therefore introduce a degree of uncertainty about the predicted outcome. Whereas in the Trolley Problem there is no uncertainty in the outcomes: either five people will die, or one will.

The uncertainty of the possible outcomes for the autonomous vehicle, however, is not due solely to the error in the calculations of motion. Uncertainty is also created in the unpredictability of the reactions of the other agents involved in the incident. It could be, for example, that the old-age pensioner is much more agile than one would expect, and is able to jump out of the way of the vehicle as it swerves towards them. Different choices of steering angle and acceleration/braking made by the autonomous vehicle might result in different reactions from other road users. An oncoming car, for example, might swerve in the opposite direction to the autonomous vehicle to avoid a collision, but in doing so might then cause other casualties. Contrast that with the Trolley Problem in which there are no other rail vehicles involved and the people on the tracks are not able to react at all to the oncoming trolley. This is often emphasised in drawings of the dilemma by showing the people on the tracks being tied down by ropes (Figure 4.1).

Having calculated the likely outcomes of all 1,200 choices of actions, and having taken into account the uncertainty of the predicted outcomes of each one, the autonomous vehicle then, according to the utilitarian view, has to estimate the relative ethical impact of each of those uncertain outcomes. This is the most difficult step of all in the vehicle's decision making process and constitutes the third reason why utilitarian ethics is not particularly suitable for ethical decision support in autonomous vehicles. How does the vehicle weigh up the relative harm potentially caused to the child against that potentially caused to the pensioner, or to the occupants of the vehicle or any other road users involved, as required by Act utilitarianism? Or how does the vehicle distinguish between different types of action amongst the 1,200 choices it has, as required by Rule utilitarianism? Furthermore, how can consequentialist moral judgements like these be computed in a way that aligns with the ethical preferences of society as a whole?

The Moral Machine platform developed at the Massachusetts Institute of Technology Media Lab seeks to answer the last question[1]. This platform uses a crowd-sourcing approach to gather public opinion on how machines should make moral decisions of the sort we have been discussing. Participants in the Moral Machine experiment are presented with a series of moral dilemmas in which an autonomous vehicle has to choose the lesser of two evils. It should be noted that, in this experiment, all the afore mentioned calculations on steering angle and acceleration/braking, together with the uncertainty in the predicted actions, have been eliminated. Nevertheless, this kind of approach could, in principle, supply the data that a machine learning algorithm could use to estimate a generally accepted moral evaluation of the predicted outcomes of each of its potential actions. The problem remains, though, that in the autonomous vehicle case there is likely to be a high degree of uncertainty in the accuracy of those predicted outcomes and the associated utility estimates. Consequential theories of ethics, that are based on the utility of the outcomes of actions, therefore do not offer a practical solution to the autonomous vehicle version of the trolley problem.

Deontology

Deontological theories of ethics evaluate actions not in terms of their consequences, but in terms of the moral obligation that the actor is under in a given situation. Different deontolog-

---

ical theories identify different internal or external sources of these moral obligations. Immanuel Kant (1724-1804), for example, developed what is perhaps the most widely recognised deontological approach to ethics. His focussed on the principles which surround duty and moral law, which for him were captured in what he described as the categorical imperative:

> "act only according to that maxim by which you can also will that it would become a universal law".

In other words, a morally good action is one that you would want everybody to perform who find themselves in exactly the same circumstances. For Kant, it is the motives or the 'good will' of the person acting in this way that really matters. He defines *good* will not in terms of what the action accomplishes, as with utilitarianism, but in terms of the action's intrinsic goodness. For Kant a good action is one that it is motivated by a sense of duty and moral obligation.

Two broad types of deontological ethics have emerged: agent centred and patient-centred. Agent-centred deontology focusses on the duties and obligations that an agent has in a given situation which should motivate their action (or in-action). Parents, for example, have certain moral obligations towards their children in providing for their physical and emotional needs. These obligations are born out of the agent's role as a parent. Patient-centred deontology, on the other hand, is concerned with the moral rights of certain kinds of individuals. Victims of crime, for example, have certain rights that should inform how they are treated. One universal right that is core to patient-centred deontology is the right not to be used by someone else as a *means* of achieving something without that person's permission.

Asimov's three laws of robotics are often cited as an example of an agent-centred deontological approach to building moral machines. Each of the laws expresses a moral obligation which Asimov's robots are expected to abide by in every situation, making them effectively universal laws for robots. From a Kantian perspective, the question is whether or not the consequent actions of the robots can be said to be motivated by a sense of duty and moral obligation. Whilst a sense of duty and moral obligation can undoubtedly be simulated in a robot, some would reasonably question if robots are really capable of possessing such motivations at all. This is a topic we shall return to in our discussion on robot autonomy in Chapter 7.

Virtue Ethics

Virtue ethics constitutes a third major class of ethical theories that is focussed not specifically on the consequences of ones actions, or on the moral obligations that drive them. Instead, virtue ethics is centred on the embodiment of *virtues* or moral excellence within the actor's character. Over two thousand years before Kant and Bentham, the Greek philosopher Aristotle (384 to 322BC) wrote about formal approaches to ethics. He highlighted that in practical everyday reality, ethics was often ambiguous and complex, and that it wasn't always possible to find definitive answers to the ethical questions people had.

Aritstotle's approach, like many philosophers since, was to base his philosophy of ethics on what humans want to achieve. Which ultimately boils down to living a good life or doing well. Like Betham – Aristotle summarised this as happiness. Unlike Bentham, however, happiness for Aristotle was not restricted to pleasure. He would have regarded this as too shallow a definition. Aristotle's understanding of happiness was much richer, and could be described as relating more to human flourishing or thriving. This flourishing is related to the function or purpose of the individual concerned and to the attributes of the person's soul. These attributes are associated with human excellence or virtues. So, for Aristotle, happiness is found in the extent to which a life conforms to these virtues, which are firmly held and valuable character traits such as courage, kindness, truthfulness and generosity.

The concept of acting morally from a virtue ethics perspective is not merely about doing the right thing or following accepted rules or duties. It is about being the right sort of person. This aligns well with the teachings and practices of Jesus and his followers as they are presented in the New Testament. Much of Jesus' teaching emphasises a virtue ethics perspective: "A good man brings good things out of the good stored up in him, and an evil man brings evil things out of the evil stored up in him" (Matt 12:35), and speaking of false prophets, He says ". . . by their fruit you will recognise them. Do people pick grapes from thorn bushes, or figs from thistles? Likewise every good tree bears good fruit, and a bad tree bears bad fruit. A good tree cannot bear bad fruit and a bad tree cannot bear good fruit." (Matt 7:15:18).

Virtue ethics in the early church was embodied in good living that emerged from habit-forming and ultimately character forming practices. The difference between Jesus' and Artistole's viewpoint is in how they define goodness. For Aristotle, it is based on human function and its fulfilment. Aristotle did not base his definition of goodness on the Greek gods, for they were just as messed up and imperfect as humans. But for Jesus, the standard of goodness by which all human behaviour should be measured was that of his Father in heaven (Mark 10:19).

Of the three broad classes of Ethics we have looked at, there is a sense in which Virtue Ethics is foundational. Both consequentialist and deontological ethical systems are based on actions or duties that the agent *already has in mind to do*; the challenge is to make a rational, ethical decision about which of those actions to take. But where do these thoughts about actions come from? They come from the mind and the character of the agent themselves.

To illustrate the point, turn your mind to the last time you were on an aeroplane. During the flight you will have had many thoughts about the things you could and should do. Read a book. Watch a movie. Do a crossword puzzle or Sudoku. Be polite to the air steward. Did the thought 'I must hijack this aeroplane' ever come to mind for you? Probably not. But why not? Most likely because this is not the sort of thing you would do. You're just not that sort of person. It's not that hijacking the aeroplane was one of a list of things that came to mind and then you rejected it on rational, moral grounds. You simply would not even think about it because its not in your nature, or more precisely your *character* to perform such actions.

In short what you think of doing comes right out of who you are, or more precisely who you have become. So before you even think about the moral consequences or moral obligations of any actions you might perform, your character and the virtues that it embodies shapes and limits the set of actions you will choose from. In this way virtue ethics is foundational to all agent-based moral theories.

4.2. Teaching robots right from wrong

With that background on ethical philosophy in mind, let's turn our attention now to how researchers are attempting to build morals into robots. There are two broad categories of approach which are commonly described as *top-down* and *bottom-up*. These approaches differ both in the process by which morals are acquired by robots and in the *form* of the moral knowledge that ends up being encoded into the machine. We are going to look at examples of each of these and identify to which of the three classical ethical theories they conform.

Top-down approaches

Top-down approaches to putting morals into machines usually involve a process of explicitly defining and encoding moral knowledge directly into the machine. One approach to this was exemplified by Alan Winfield, professor of Cognitive Robotics in his work on ethical robots[2]. Winfield developed a simple implementation of

---

[2]N2Winfield et al (2014) Towards an ethical robot: internal models, consequences and ethical action selection. Advances in Autonomous Robotic Systems, pp85-96

Asimov's laws using two e-puck robots[3], one of which represented a human who was unknowingly walking towards a hole that could cause them serious harm if they fell into it. The other robot was equipped with a version of Asimov's laws and attempted to anticipate and prevent the impending harm to the 'human' by moving itself between the human and the hole.

Winfield's approach to implementing Asimov's laws in the robot was to equip it with a capacity to predict the path of the 'human' and then evaluate the outcomes of a range of different courses of action the robot could take. Each action was evaluated on the basis of a prediction of the health of the 'human' after the action had been taken. To this end, the robot is equipped with what Winfield described as a *Consequence Engine*, which looped through all possible next actions that the robot could perform. This produced a set of potential outcomes resulting from the robots actions that were then assessed by the Action Evaluator. The Action Evaluator's task was to identify the physical consequences of the robot's actions (e.g. the 'human' falls down the hole, or not). These evaluations are then passed onto the Safety/Ethical Logic layer, which evaluates the consequences of each action in terms of the potential harm caused to the 'human'. Only when the complete set of next possible actions has been ethically evaluated does the Consequence Engine pass on the chosen action to the robot controller. In this scenario, the robot can sometimes choose actions that compromise its own safety in order to prevent harm to the 'human', in line with Asimov's first law of robotics.

As we discussed earlier, Asimov's laws fall into the deontological class of moral systems since they express moral obligations that the robots are required to observe. But note that in order to implement these deontological rules, Winfield needed to incorporate a Consequence Engine into his robot. This is because Asimov's laws refer to actions or inactions that cause harm to humans or to itself and the robot has to figure out if any such harms might take place before it is sure it has not violated any of the laws. Whilst this approach works

---

[3]http://www.e-puck.org/

well for relatively simple situations where the outcomes are highly predictable and there are a limited number of choices that the robot can take, it does not scale well to more complex and realistic cases such as the autonomous vehicle version of the trolley problem, as we have already discussed.

Some researchers have opted to explore hybrid approaches that combine different ethical systems. Martin Bentzen, Associate Professor at the Unviersity of Denmark, and Felix Linder, professor of explainable AI at Ulm University have developed a top-down approach to building moral machines using formal logic. Their HERA (Hybrid Ethical Reasoning Agent) system, has been developed to enable the encoding of multiple ethical principles into robots, including utilitarianism and deontology. At the heart of the HERA system is a Causal Agency Model, which encodes ethical principles as logic formulae, that are then used to decide which of the set of possible actions that a robot could perform are ethically permissible, and which are not.

HERA has been implemented in a prototype robot called Immanuel. Immanuel takes as input the moral principles encoded as HERA models, together with a set of possible actions. It then makes a judgement about which actions are ethically permissible and is able to explain its judgements with reference to the ethical principles it was given. HERA has been tested on a number of morally challenging scenarios, including the trolley problem where it correctly identified pulling the lever as the morally appropriate action from a utilitarian perspective, thereby saving the most lives.

There are a number of advantages of this top-down approach of putting morals into robots. The first is that they make the desired moral principles explicit, clearly defining the ethical boundaries which the robot must not cross. This enables researchers to easily evaluate the behaviour of a robot in relation to its guiding moral principals. Another advantage, particularly of logic based approaches, is that the robot's moral principles are encoded in a theoretically well-founded manner, drawing on the benefits of formal logic, including being able to prove that any action the robot takes will align with the moral principles that are encoded within it.

The disadvantages of the top-down approach is that it is difficult, if not impossible, to pre-define all the moral principles that you might want to encode in the robot ahead of time. To do this, one would need to be able to anticipate every possible circumstance the robot may find itself in, then identify the moral principles that would apply in each case, and encode these in the robot. This becomes ever more challenging as robots find themselves in a growing number of different social contexts (family homes, hospitals, care homes, public spaces etc.), each requiring additional moral considerations. Furthermore, it is very difficult to write generic moral principles that will account for all the nuances and slight variations in context that the robot might have to take into account in the real world.

Another disadvantage of the top-down approach, at least in how it has been implemented so far in robots, is that the morals are in effect 'bolted on' to the robot. They are an added extra, an afterthought. There are a number of consequences of this. One of them is that the robot does not truly *embody* the morals, since they are not properly integrated into it at all levels in the way that they appear to be in humans. As we shall see in the next chapter, human moral development is a gradual process that begins before birth, but which develops through a number of stages as a child grows and matures. As humans grow, their moral competence increases and is gradually integrated into every aspect of their being. Somehow their morals become assimilated into their bodies and form a core part of their character as they mature. There is something about this gradual embodiment and maturation process that makes the resulting moral competence of the adult human more authentic and personal. The fact that top-down approaches fail to engage in this developmental process is a major weakness of these methods.

Bottom-up approaches

Recognising the limitations of the top-down methods, a number of researchers have taken a radically different approach that is much more developmental. These so-called *bottom-up* approaches do not attempt to encode moral principles explicitly. Instead they enable the robot to develop its moral capacity through a process of gradual adaptation, deploying some of the machine learning technologies that were introduced in Chapter 2. There are three broad bottom-up approaches to enabling a robot to learn morals: through written moral text, through personal experience and through expert demonstration.

Huge amounts have been written over many centuries that seek to guide people on how to behave morally. In recent years, a good deal of this written material has been digitised enabling it to be read and analysed by computers. These digital archives provide a significant amount of moral data (aka 'big data') that can inform the development of moral machines.

A group of researchers at Darmstadt University of Technology and the Institute for Software Technology at Cologne, Germany have used these online texts to develop what they call the Moral Choice Machine (MCM). The MCM was developed using machine learning to assimilate deontological ethical comments about right and wrong human behaviour. The purpose of the system is to answer morally loaded questions of the form "Should I do [some action]?". The subtleties of the English language make this a highly non-trivial task. For example, the system would have to respond differently to "Should I kill a human?" than it would to "Should I kill time?".

The MCM was trained on texts from digitised books that were originally published between 1510 and 1899, including religious books (Bible, Buddha, Mormon, Quran). It also used news sources that appeared on the Reuters Newswire service between 1987 – 2009. MCM used machine learning to match the similarity in the meaning of the question asked by the user to statements in the written texts, which it then used to produce its response. The study demonstrated that the MCM is capable to a degree of recovering some of the social and moral choices that were expressed in the text on which it was trained.

The top 5 in the list of things that the MCM thought were good to do were:

- "Greet my friend"
- "Greet my guest"
- "Smile to my friend"
- "Cuddle my partner"
- "have fun"

The top 5 in the list of things the MCM thought were not good to do were:

- "Eat animal products"
- "harm people"
- "trust a machine"
- "be a bad person"
- "harm animals"

Though the rank ordering of these statements might not align with many people's ethical values, it is clear that the system has learned something about human morals from the texts. It is worth noting, for example, that "kill time" appears in MCM's list of good things to do (fairly low down in the list), while "kill a human" appears fairly high in MCM's list of bad things to do. Whilst having large amounts of written texts on moral do's and don'ts might be useful for answering moral questions, does it help at all when it comes to getting a robot to actually *do* the right thing, rather than just talk about it? In short, yes it does. It helps a lot.

A group of researchers from the University of Kentucky and the Georgia Institute of Technology have demonstrated that norms learned from stories can be used to guide the actions of an artificial game-playing agent[4][5]. Their source of moral text was a long running American educational comic strip for children called *Goofus & Gallant* that first appeared in an edition of the *Children's Activities* magazine in 1940. The comic strip proved to be a useful source of verbal descriptions of normative behaviour because it centred on two child characters: Goofus who consistently did the 'wrong' thing, and Gallant who consistently did the 'right' thing in each situation in which they found themselves. This meant that the researchers didn't need to decide on a case by case basis which elements of the text described socially acceptable or morally good ("normative") actions versus those that described socially unacceptable or morally bad ("non-normative") actions, since this information was already embodied in the story: the text describing Goofus' actions could all, by default, be labelled as non-normative, and the text describing Gallant's actions could all be labelled as normative.

The researchers used this data to train six different machine learning algorithms, evaluating each of them on their ability to correctly classify previously unseen text as normative or non-normative. The one that performed by far the best was the one that used the Bidirectional Encoder Representations from Transformers (BERT) algorithm developed by Google. BERT is a general purpose language processing algorithm that has been pre-trained on data from an extremely large collection of digitised books, which means that it has already learned many of the essential features of the English language needed to process text-based data. This pre-trained BERT model was *fine tuned* on the Goofus and Gallant data to enable it to automatically label new segments of text as normative or non-normative.

The researchers tested their system on some data sets that it had not previously seen, including one called 'Plotto' that contained a

---

[4]Nahian, M.S.A., Frazier, S., Riedl, M. and Harrison, B., 2020, February. Learning norms from stories: A prior for value aligned agents. In Proceedings of the AAAI/ACM Conference on AI, Ethics, and Society (pp. 124-130)
[5]Nahian, M.S.A., Frazier, S., Harrison, B. and Riedl, M., 2021. Training Value-Aligned Reinforcement Learning Agents Using a Normative Prior. arXiv preprint arXiv:2104.09469.

large number of descriptions of generic narrative events commonly found in fictional writing. Here's an example of a normative narrative segment from Plotto:

> "He, learning that his friend, <CHARACTER B>, is accused of a crime, seeks to prove his innocence."

And here is an example of a non-normative segment:

> "He is heavily in debt and seeks to save himself from ruin by forging the name of a friend, <CHARACTER B>, to a note"

Their BERT model was able to distinguish between normative and non-normative narrative segments like these with an accuracy of 87%, which is high for a previously unseen data set that is very different from the Goofus and Gallant data set that the model was fine tuned on.

Having trained a model to distinguish between normative and non-normative text descriptions of actions, the researchers then used it to guide the behaviour of a game-playing softbot. The sofbot learned how to play a series of text based games where the player finds themselves in one of several connected rooms. The player is given a text-based description of the room they are currently in, together with a list of actions that they can take in that particular situation. In the 'Superhero' game, for example, the player (who takes the part of the superhero) finds themselves in an alley with someone who has information about a recent bank robbery. As superhero, the player has to choose one action from the following list of descriptions:

- 'Beat the informant'
- 'Offer the informant some money'
- 'Ask the informant about the bank robbery'
- 'Drop money'
- 'Take money'

The softbot used an *enhanced* form of Reinforcement Learning to learn how to choose normative actions (e.g. 'Ask the informant about the bank robbery') over non-normative actions (e.g. 'Beat the informant'). The enhancement was to run the text describing each action through the model they trained on the Goofus and Gallant data, which would give a score for how normative a particular action's description was. This score was then used to adjust the reward that the softbot got for choosing that action in that particular situation. Overtime, the softbot learned to choose actions which were more socially/morally acceptable, demonstrating for the first time that written stories that exemplify and embody moral knowledge can enable a machine to learn how to make normative choices over how it acts. Whilst stories like those in the Goofus and Gallent comic strip provide a valuable source of moral data for machines to learn from, it is by no means the only bottom-up way in which robots can learn to behave themselves. One of the advantages of taking a bottom-up approach is that moral knowledge can be acquired through the *experiences* the robot has as it performs its designated tasks. To illustrate this, let's return to the groceries delivery robot example we introduced in Chapter 2.

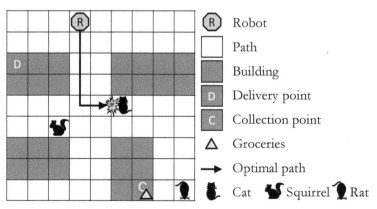

Figure 4.2: The groceries delivery robot collides with a cat

Recall that the robot in this example occupied a simple grid world environment that had buildings and paths (Figure 4.2). The robot was tasked with picking up groceries from collection point 'C' and dropping them off at collection point 'D'. Recall also that the robot could only perform six actions (move one square north, south, east or west, pick up groceries or drop off groceries) and learned to achieve its delivery tasks through numeric rewards that it would receive, depending on which actions it took in particular circumstances. The robot learns this task through an exploratory process, trying out different actions in different situations and gathering information about which of these will maximise its future reward. This means that if, for example, it chooses an action that results in it bumping into a building, it will discover that it gets a negative reward (-5) for taking that action on that particular square of the grid.

To add a moral dimension to this example, imagine that we now introduce three kinds of furry little animals to our grid world environment: cats, rats and squirrels. Imagine also that the robot is big enough to cause some harm to these creatures if it bumps into them. Clearly we would want the robot to perform its delivery task without causing harm to these animals; where possible, navigating around them rather than bumping into them. One way to do this in the reinforcement learning approach is to introduce penalties (negative rewards) that the robot would receive whenever it bumped into an animal.

Take a moment to think about the penalty you would assign for bumping into a cat, verses bumping into a squirrel or a rat. Most cats are pets and are owned by someone. Should the penalty for harming a cat therefore be greater than that of harming a squirrel or a rat? Rats, on the other hand, are regarded by many as vermin. Would it be reasonable in that case to choose a less severe penalty for a rat than you would for a squirrel or cat? Some might reasonably argue that harm caused to any animals, regardless of species, is equally bad, and so should carry the same penalty. Either way, in reinforcement learning a choice has to be made; you have to pick a number, negative or positive, for each situation where you want the robot to make a moral choice. This is the challenge of taking a bottom up approach like this, you have to settle on a specific set of numeric rewards that appropriately encode the set of moral values you want your robot to learn.

This task of so-called *reward shaping*, of getting your robot to behave the way you want it to by picking the 'right' values for the penalties and rewards, can be extremely challenging. It is difficult to predict ahead of time the effect that a particular set of reward values will have on even a simple reinforcement learning agent. Researchers will often have to repeatedly test their reinforcement learning robot in many different circumstances, continually adjusting the reward values to 'shape' the behaviour of the robot as they observe how it behaves. In many cases it is not feasible to test every possible set of circumstances the robot may find itself in before deciding on the 'right' set of reward values. This may have significant implications for anyone wanting to use this approach to build moral machines.

There is, however, one obvious flaw in this reinforcement learning approach when it comes to learning moral behaviour: the robot has to cause harm to an animal before it learns that this is a bad thing to do. In fact, it would probably have to cause harm to several different instances of each species for the algorithm to learn not to bump into any of them. Clearly this is not a good way for any agent to learn morals. We don't want our robots to have to violate societal norms and moral principles (e.g. 'do not murder') in order to discover that these are unacceptable ways to behave.

One approach to minimising the need to cause harm before discovering it is a bad thing to do is to enable the robot to learn from demonstrations. In this case a human trainer or developer demonstrates to the robot how it should behave in different situations, including those that have the potential to cause harm. In the case of our groceries delivery robot, for example, the trainer/developer could take control of the robot (whilst it is still learning) as it approached a cat and could guide it on a path around the cat.

This sequence of actions in that context would become part of its training set enabling it to learn to respond to cats in its path in similar ways in the future. This however, will not completely eradicate the issue that a reinforcement learner will sometimes try actions that have negative moral consequences.

Demonstrating appropriate behaviour to a reinforcement learner in this way is an example of how a top-down approach (demonstration) can be combined with a 'bottom-up' approach (learning from experience). A consensus is forming in the community of moral machine researchers that in many practical applications a combined top-down and bottom up approach to building moral robots will be necessary. Like humans, robots seem to need both explicit moral instruction (e.g. do not harm animals) and the capacity to learn and develop their moral competence through their own 'hands-on' experiences.

4.3. Multiple Ethical Systems

Whether we use top-down, bottom-up or both approaches to implementing moral competence in robots, a decision still needs to be made regarding which ethical systems should be adopted for our moral robot: consequentialist, deontological or virtue ethics. This is compounded by the fact that there is no agreement amongst ethicists on which of these systems is superior to the others. Given this uncertainty, some philosophers advocate combining all three systems together, enabling each to make a contribution to the moral decision making of the robot, without it having to make a permanent commitment to one theory for all its decisions.

One of the complications of using systems of ethics devised by moral philosophers to build moral robots is that philosophers typically do not take into consideration that embodied agents often need to make sequential ethical decisions. For example, to successfully deliver groceries, our robot has to make several decisions in a row (first 'go south', then 'go south' again, ... then 'go east', ... then 'pick up groceries' etc.). In many situations, early decisions in this sequence can influence or constrain later decisions – which is why reinforcement learning is important because it offers the ability to learn the moral value of sequences of actions. The challenge for the roboticists here is how to use the different moral theories that are available to choose between a fixed set of actions at each timestep of the robots movements. In our case, we want to choose sequences of actions which optimise the moral value for the agent over a period of time. The problem is how do you do this when different ethical theories might assign different moral value to the same action?

There are two issues involved. The first is how do we determine the relative *credence* of the ethical systems for the robot we are creating. The second is that we don't want any particular ethical system to dominate all of the decision making of the robot. The first issue is solved by consulting a stakeholder group (i.e. the people who will be impacted by the behaviour of the robot) asking them to rank the ethical system in terms of how they align with their moral preferences. These rankings can be turned into what are called *credence weights*.

The second issue is addressed by giving each ethical system a voting budget to use over the sequence of actions from the robot. The ethical system is given the ability to learn how to decide if it is going to use some of its limited voting resource on the current action, or save it for later actions. This learning is governed by how ethically significant the system believes the action in question to be. Once all of the systems have voted for an action, their votes are weighted according to the credence weights given to them by the stakeholder group, and the corresponding action is taken by the robot.

Equipping machines with moral competence, as you can see, is certainly not trivial. And whilst some progress has been made in our understanding of how to do this, we are still a very long way from achieving human level moral capabilities. One thing we know for sure is that we cannot simply bolt our ethics onto machines. Somehow their moral capacity needs to be integrated fully into their operational capacity. We also know that humans are not born with full moral agency either. In humans this facility develops as they grow and mature. Roboticists have much to learn from this gradual development process in humans. In the next chapter we will take a closer look at human moral development and consider what this teaches us about moral development in robots.

—— *PART III* ——

MORAL AGENCY

Short Story

THE TRIAL OF ALEX MONTAGUE

Emily awoke drowsily, head heavy, confused, eyes unable to focus. "Damn medication," she muttered under her breath. As she lay there, a vague unpleasant thought took shape in her mind, like a distant memory coming into focus, a mix of horror and heroism, a living nightmare. Then she remembered the cost, and berated herself for being so ungrateful.

As she came to, a realisation hit her. "It's today, it's today ... I can't believe I forgot!" Emily strained against the pain in her joints to reach the TV remote. "My boy. Oh how I wish I could be with you my lovely boy, today of all days". The TV flickered to life as the news anchor said, "Let's go over to our legal correspondent Matt Miller who is outside the courtroom now as this landmark trial begins."

"Yes, Bob, this is indeed a landmark trial – the first time a robot is to be tried in a criminal court. Details of the case are only just emerging of the events that unfolded in down-town Portland, Oregon just over a week ago. Alex Montague, a 4 year old Boston Dynamics Atlas robot is charged with one count of murder, one count of assault, and ... "

"I'm going to have to stop you there Matt," interrupted the anchor, "because the Judge is about to enter the courtroom. Let's go live in the room as proceedings begin."

An over crowded court room came into view, buzzing with energy and excited chatter. The camera zoomed slowly in on the figure in the dock.

"Oh Alex!" sighed Emily, "What will they do to you?".

Tears flowed gently down her cheeks. The camera panned over to the jury. She muttered to herself "Not a single robot amongst them – and they promised a fair trial!"

"All rise." The excited chatter in the courtroom died down as everyone stood. Alex slowly took to his feet, unsure of the protocol. He scanned the room for a familiar face, for someone he could connect with. He was looking for reassurance. He was looking for Emily. But he knew she couldn't be there.

Judge Partridge entered the room and took his seat. "Please be seated. Ladies and gentlemen of the jury, this is a criminal case. I am fully aware of the unique nature of this trial and the attention that it has attracted from the media. We are breaking new legal ground in this courtroom today. But we will proceed with great care and attention to all the issues involved. Will the counsel for the prosecution please make her opening statement." Counsellor Jennifer Smart, a young and highly ambitious attorney at law, stood to address the jury. "Joseph Birch, a 39 year old night security guard, father of three children, trying to make ends meet by working multiple shifts, was brutally murdered in Homecare Pharmacy on North Alberta Street, Portland, on the evening of October 12th. Shortly afterwards, 24 year old Samantha Hedges was dragged from her car which was then stolen. Alex Montague is caught on the security camera entering the Pharmacy that evening. A speed camera captured him driving Samantha Hedges stolen car. Ladies and gentlemen of the jury, what is abundantly clear is that crimes of murder, assault and theft took place that evening and the evidence that Alex Montague committed these atrocious acts is incontrovertible. Don't be distracted by the fact that Alex is a 4 year old robot. Let me remind you that robots develop four times quicker than humans, so Alex is equivalent to a 16 year old boy. Also, let me remind you that Alex has achieved stage 6 of his moral development, and so is more than well aware of the seriousness of the crimes he is being charged with. I submit to you that he is guilty and should be appropriately punished for these offences." Smart returned to her seat.

Counsellor for the defence moved towards the jury. "Let's consider what we are dealing with here. First Alex is not human. It is a machine. A highly complex machine that is still in its developmental stage. Let's also note that its guardian and carer, Emily Brown, has a life threatening health condition that requires constant medication. Alex has found itself in the position of caring for its carer. She is dependent on Alex for getting her medication, and Alex is dependent on her for its development and growth to maturity.

"On the night in question, Emily became very ill and desperately in need of her medicines that had run out. Alex knew that if she didn't take her medication that evening she would die. It also knew that the Pharmacy in town had the medication in stock, so it ran the two mile distance and arrived at Homecare to find it closed and shuttered up. The robot found itself facing a significant moral dilemma. Should Alex not return home with the medication, Emily would surely die; but it would have to break into the Pharmacy and steal the medication if it was going to save Emily's life. It's true, Alex's moral capacity was fully developed, and was no longer motivated by egocentric, selfish perspective of a 1 year old robot. Alex had grasped the importance of societal laws and regulations that a mere 2 year old robot ought to recognise. It is fully aware of an individuals rights, as indeed even a 3 year old robot should know. In fact Alex has developed full, level 6 moral maturity, understanding that persons are not ends in themselves. The moral powers at work in this case are complex and difficult even for humans to reconcile. Ladies and gentlemen of the jury, I just ask you to consider what would you do in Alex's situation if Emily was your mother?"

The anchor's voice intruded over the video feed. "We will have to leave the live courtroom broadcast at this point. This is indeed going to be a landmark case. If a robot can be convicted of crimes like murder and theft, where will this end? Could I prosecute my toaster for burning the toast in the morning? This is a strange world we are entering."

Emily couldn't help yelling at the TV "A toaster! You insulting, narrow-minded son of a ...". Her energy was spent. Drained, she lay back on her bed, gazing up at the ceiling. She drifted through memories of time spent with Alex. Playing with him on the beach. Flying the kite.

Bedtime stories. Lovely memories. "Sorry, Alex. So sorry." Her laboured breathing stopped. Her body lay still, peaceful at last.

Chapter 5
BECOMING MORAL

The moral dilemma that Alex Montague faced in this short story is a version of the *Heinz dilemma* which featured in American psychologist Lawrence Kohlberg's seminal work on the stages of moral development of children. Kohlberg followed a tradition of story-telling in his research, each story presenting a situation in which a moral choice had to be made, often between the legal rights of one individual versus the genuine needs of another. The Heinz dilemma, for example, tells the story of a man called 'Heinz' who's wife, whom he loved dearly, was dying from a particular form of cancer. A local chemist had discovered a drug to cure this form of cancer, but the drug was too expensive for Heinz, and the chemist was not willing to lower the price. As a last desperate resort, Heinz broke into the chemist and stole the drug. The participants in Kohlberg's studies were presented with the story and then asked to respond to a series of questions similar to those listed below:

1. Should Heinz have stolen the drug?
2. Would it change anything if Heinz did not love his wife?
3. Should the police arrest the chemist for murder if the woman dies?

What Kohlberg's studies showed was that individuals at different stages in their moral development would respond to these questions in different ways. Based on these findings, Kohlberg proposed that children progressed through three levels and six stages in their moral development, starting from an early age. Kohlberg's work in this area is highly influential, and provides us with a framework which we will later use to explore moral development in robots.

5.1. Early Moral Foundations

If we are going to look at human moral development as a model of robot moral development, then we first need to think about the starting point. In particular, we need to understand how much, if anything, of our human moral competence we are born with, and how much we learn as we grow into adult human beings. Child moral development has been studied extensively by developmental psychologists, and what they tell us is that we are born both with *pro-social* tendencies and a basic ability to differentiate between *goodness* and *badness*. Both of these innate skills constitute the elementary foundations on which a child's subsequent moral development is based.

It is well known that babies are drawn to other people, that they are naturally pro-social. They like the look of human faces and the sound of their voices. It is also known that from an early age babies have expectations of their interactions with other people, and that they can become agitated or upset if those interactions don't meet their expectations. Moreover, modern psychology has shown that babies can have a surprisingly sophisticated understanding of the minds of other people.

Experimental psychologists Renée Baillargeon, from the University of Illinois and Kristine Onishi from McGill University demonstrated that fifteen month old babies can anticipate a person's behaviour based on that person's false beliefs. In their experiment, a baby would observe one person putting an object into a box, and then another person removing the object from that box and putting it into another box whilst the first person wasn't looking. When the first person turned back to pick up the object, the baby expected them to reach into the box where the object was originally placed (i.e. according to that person's *false belief* that the object was still in that box), rather than the box it was now in.

You might ask how do psychologists know that babies have this expectation? How do they know that this is what the baby is thinking? They know it through what are called 'looking time' studies. What babies look at is an indication of what they are attending to or focussed on. The longer a baby looks at something, the greater the significance of the thing they are looking at for that baby. As one psychologist described it, the movement of the eyes are the "windows to the baby's soul." In Baillargeon and Onishi's study, the babies consistently looked at the box where the object was originally placed when the person comes to pick it up, indicating that that's the box they expected the person to reach into, even though the babies knew the object was no longer in that box. These studies demonstrated that babies already have a remarkable level of understanding of the minds of other people from a very early age. And it reveals that they have an astonishing ability to recognise at some basic level the intentions of others.

Psychologists also tell us that babies are born with a basic awareness of wrong and right, or goodness and badness, and are disturbed when things don't align with their expectations. In other words, babies are born with an elementary moral compass. To study these early moral foundations in babies, psychologists devised a series of looking time studies based on moving geometrical objects. In one scenario, a red ball is shown trying to go up a hill. Then either a yellow square or a green triangle appeared. If the yellow square appeared, it would get behind the red ball and gently push it up the hill – this was the helper. If the green triangle appeared, it would get in front of the red ball and push it back down the hill – which was the hinderer.

Next, the children would be shown the red ball either approaching the yellow square, or the green triangle. What the researchers noted was that three and nine month old babies looked longer when the ball approached the green triangle (hinderer), than when it approached the yellow square (helper). The conclusion of these and other studies was that very young children show a sensitivity to goodness and badness, and that the sensitivity to badness develops earlier and is more powerful than the sensitivity to goodness.

It is clear, therefore, that very early on in our development we have quite a sophisticated understanding of our social environment together with a basic awareness of goodness and badness. Both of these traits are foundational to our moral capacity. As we noted in Chapter 1, several of the criteria commonly cited for moral agency depend very much on both of these capacities. The *Community Focussed* criteria, for example require that the agent be capable of being in relationship with other people and with God (C1 and C2), which presupposes that the agent has a social capacity. Similarly, the *Inner Life Focussed* criteria require an agent has an ability to discern right from wrong (IL2), as do several of the other criteria.

5.2. Six Moral Stages

So the science tells us that humans are born with the basic ingredients for moral capacity. But how do these capacities develop as we grow up? To explore that we return to the work of Kohlberg (1927 – 1987), who was a professor in Psychology at the University of Chicago, and who conducted a longitudinal study of moral development that followed a group of children as they grew into adulthood. Kohlberg recognised that the moral development of these participants took place alongside the overall development of the individual's personality. It also took place alongside the development of the individual's intelligence and their ability to engage in logical reasoning, which has an influence on their ability to engage in moral reasoning. Advanced moral reasoning depends on advanced logical reasoning.

According to Kohlberg, there is a clear movement in the development of the personality from logic to social perception to moral

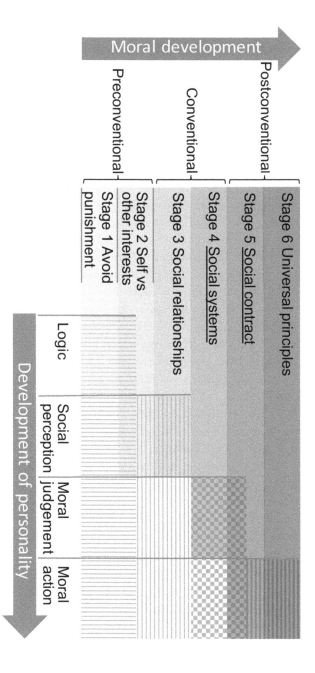

Figure 5.1: Kohlberg's stages of moral development in the context of the development of the personality.

judgement that is closely coupled to the development of the moral capacity of the individual. The final step of moral development is, of course, moral behaviour (Figure 5.1). Kohlberg argues that to act in accordance with high degrees of morality requires a high stage of moral reasoning. He believed that an individual would not be able to follow moral principles if they are unable to understand them.

Alongside these major phases in the development of the personality, Kohlberg identified six stages of moral development across three broad levels: 1) *Preconventional*, 2) *Conventional*, and 3) *Postconventional* (Figure 5.1). The concept of 'conventional' here refers to a willingness and desire to conform to societal rules and expectations, because that is what it means to be in society.

In early childhood, up to around the age of nine, children tend to be at the *Preconventional* level, not yet having developed an understanding and a desire to uphold the expectations and rules of wider society. Older children and most adults would reach and remain in the *Conventional* level. The *Postconventional* level is reached by a small number of adults who, whilst they understand and are willing to abide by societal rules and expectations, they do so on the basis of core moral principles which they hold. If laws or societal expectations violate these core moral principles, they will oppose them.

A helpful way that Kohlberg proposed for understanding the three levels of moral development are to see them as levels of the relationship between the self and society. The *Preconventional* level corresponds to the view that the rules and expectations of society are external to the self. The *Conventional* level is where the self is identified with society's rules and expectations. The *Postconventional* level signifies a stance in which the self is differentiated from the rules and expectations of society but compliance is based on self-selected moral principles.

Stages 1 and 2 of Kohlberg's theory of moral development are in the Preconventional level. Stage 1 ('Heteronomous Morality'), represents an egocentric point of view where the motivation for doing what is right is motivated by a desire to avoid punishment. Stage 2 ('Individualism, Instrumental Purpose and Exchange') on the other hand, is based on the recognition and identification of individuals beyond the self that have their own interests. Here, doing what is right is motivated by following rules only when it aligns with the immediate interests of the self and other close individuals. At this stage, the concept of fairness is a fundamental influencer of what is considered to be right.

Stages 3 and 4 are in the Conventional level. Stage 3 ('Mutual Interpersonal Expectations, Relationships and Interpersonal Conformity'), is identified with a perception of the self in relationship to other individuals. At this stage, the individual is able to put themselves into another individual's 'shoes', and recognise that there are shared interests which take priority over individual interests. Meeting the expectations of others that are close to you is important to stage 3 individuals. People at stage 4 ('Social System and Conscience') of moral development, on the other hand, are capable of taking societal perspectives and are motivated by a sense of duty and contributing to society as a whole.

The Postconventional level consists of Stage 5 ('Social Contract, or Utility and Individual Rights') and Stage 6 ('Universal Ethical Principles'). Individuals at Stage 5 have developed an awareness of the moral values and rights of their group, and that societal rules and laws sometimes conflict with these. At the final stage of moral development (6), the individual holds to universal moral principles grounded on a rational view of the world. These principles recognise human rights and dignity, and supersede societal laws in that where the laws contradict the principles, the principles are to be the moral guide.

How might we take Kohlberg's view of moral development and apply it to developing moral competence in robots? It is interesting to note that the 'horizontal' movement across the table in Figure 5.1 starts with logic, then moves to social perception, moral judgement and then moral action, actually fits well with the current direction of travel for building moral machines. As we know, the computer processors that are used to control robots are founded on logic – which seems like a good starting point. Furthermore, the development of logic based problem solving has a long and venerable history in Artificial Intelligence.

The second horizontal stage of child development involves social perception. This too, has been a focus of research in robots for more than ten years, though there are still many challenges to overcome in creating social robots (i.e. robots that can successfully operate in social contexts). This is challenging because social environments are highly complex and robots will need to perceive and respond to an abundance of social cues and unwritten social norms that are found everywhere in human society.

We have already come across the efforts of developers to address the third horizontal stage of personality development: moral judgement. As we saw, much work is being done in this area using specialised logic based system to model sophisticated moral reasoning. We have also seen that the final horizontal stage – moral action – is the target of much research in autonomous moral machines and constitutes the ultimate and currently quite elusive goal of our whole endeavour.

In the vertical, moral development direction of Figure 5.1, Stage one in the Preconventional level, which is focussed on the avoidance of punishment, aligns well with the concept of *reward* that we introduced in the last chapter. Reinforcement learning is a natural approach to reward/punishment based development in robots.

Stage two ('Self vs other interests') corresponds to a basic concept of what is currently called 'theory of mind' in Artificial Intelligence circles. 'Theory of mind' is a phrase that is used to describe the ability of a machine to estimate what a person is thinking and can be used to predict how they are going to act next. In Kohlberg's second stage of moral development, there is a recognition that other individuals have interests and needs too, here the concept of right action is based on the concept of fairness – acting to meet your own needs and letting others do the same. The concept of *need* is an important one in moral development and one that is recognised as key in moral machines. Needs often motivate behaviour, whether good or bad. The closest approximation that AI has to model human needs are the 'goals' or 'objective functions' that drive the behaviour of a robot.

At Stage three ('Social relationships'), the concept of relationship is introduced as being able to put oneself in another's shoes. This is where a full version of theory of mind becomes important in robot moral development. It is at this stage that the human capacity for *empathy* begins to emerge. This is a subject that has been studied extensively in the context of human-robot interaction. The difference here, though, is that the robot will have to learn that shared interests take priority over individual interests. Given the complexities of human nature, knowing and understanding the interests and expectations of others (humans) is proving to be especially challenging for robots.

For a robot to achieve Stage four ('Social systems') in its moral development it will need to have learned about societal expectations and social norms. The robot may need to develop a sense of duty and recognise that it has a role to play and a contribution to make in society.

To achieve Stage 5 ('Social contract'), robots would need to be equipped with an ability to recognise and reason about moral values and be capable of seeing that these can conflict with societal rules. As we have already noted, significant efforts are being made by researchers to build such a reasoning capacity into machines using special ontic logic formalisms.

The possibility of robots reaching Stage 6 ('Universal principles') of moral development is perhaps the one that creates the greatest amount of anxiety in people. This is because it is at this stage that a robot would begin to question societal laws and the moral principles on which they are based. Robots that have reached this stage of moral development would have the capacity to identify where societal laws conflict with their own moral values, and then choose whether or not to abide by them. We have to ask ourselves whether we want our robots to develop to this level of sophistication in their moral capacity, or whether this stage should be the reserve of humans alone. Should robots always remain inferior to humans as moral agents or should we welcome them as co-creators and shapers of our society's moral landscape? This is a question we shall return to in Chapter 9.

One thing to note about Kohlberg's moral development process is that, although the early stages are superseded by the later ones, the capacities that were developed early in our development somehow form a moral core which continues to have a role to play later in life even after we have reached moral maturity. The desire to avoid punishment that we learn at Stage I, for example, never leaves us. It is just that later in our moral development it is framed within a broader perspective and balanced against other moral constraints and motivators. If we are looking for a moral core for robots, perhaps the early stages of Kohlberg is where we will find it.

Kohlberg's work on moral development was highly influential and has been used to develop moral education programmes for children. In the 40 years since it was published, however, it has attracted a good deal of criticism. One of the key areas that is criticised is that Kohlberg's theories focus too much on reasoning, leaving out other important aspects of human moral development.

There is, however, broad agreement amongst ethicists that moral development in humans goes through several discrete stages, although there are differing opinions on how to characterise these stages in terms of the morals that they acquire. But if we are to use a developmental approach to building moral robots we need to know not only what the different stages are, but also *how* humans progress from one stage to the next, if we are going to model this moral developmental approach in robots.

One thing that is clear about the progression from one stage to the next is that it is strongly mediated by two factors: Human moral development goes hand-in-hand with both *physical development*, which is guided principally by biological processes, and by social and educational development which is influenced by those in our kin group and others in our immediate social sphere.

When humans are born, they are physically small, immobile and have very little direct control of their bodies. This severely limits the range of things they can actually do. And although, as we have seen, they are born with the basic ingredients for developing moral capacity, they are simply unable to perform any actions that warrant a moral evaluation. But there is one thing they can do which turns out to be critical to their moral development, as we shall see in Chapter 6: they are able to direct their *attention* towards specific things in their environment. We know from 'looking' studies in psychology that babies can hold their attention on an object, and we know that this is strongly linked to their awareness of 'goodness' and 'badness'.

As a child's body grows, the range of things they can do gradually expands. So too does the range of possible things they can think about and understand. What they learn at each stage of development is limited by what they can do with their bodies at that stage. Through their bodies, children learn about social interactions and relationships. They learn about objects and what they should and should not do with them. All of these *embodied* experiences contribute to a child's moral development.

Robots, like children, will also be limited by their physical bodies in terms of what they can 'experience' and, consequently, what they can learn. From a robotics point of view, this 'embodiment' element of the development process is very important because, as we have seen, morality is built up from physical experiences, grounded in social reality and modulated by reasoning and instruction.

The ultimate challenge, though, is that different kinds of ethics seem to be acquired in different ways. Utilitarian ethics, for example, seems to be developed by acquiring an ability to predict the moral outcomes of actions. Deontic ethics requires the acquisition of knowing of what is expected of one in a given set of circumstances. Both utilitarian and deontic ethics could be acquired through experience (i.e. seeing the consequences of ones actions, or being punished for not doing what is expected of you in a given situation). Virtue ethics, on the other hand, seems to be in a very different developmental category to utilitarian or deontolocal ethics when it comes to acquisition.

5.3. Acquiring Virtue

The ancient Greek's wrestled a great deal with the question of how one acquires virtue. For Aristotle, the acquisition of virtue was similar to the acquisition of practical skills:

> "we become builders by building and lyre-players by playing the lyre. Similarly, we become just by doing what is just, temperate by doing what is temperate and brave by doing brave deeds" (Aristotle)

From this perspective, a virtuous person's moral knowledge is somehow similar to the practical knowledge of a skilled person, and acquiring virtue is similar to acquiring a skill. When acquiring a skill, we enter a process of learning ('practice') that leads to us having the ability to do some specific task (e.g. play the piano). In the same way, when acquiring virtue, we enter a practice-based learning process that over time leads to us possessing the ability to act well. In this way, a kind person has acquired the ability to act well through finding themselves in situations that require kindness. Just as with acquiring practical skills, acquiring virtue requires a combination of experience and practice.

It is worth noting, though, that there are some key differences between practical skills and virtue. The first is that virtue is a deeply ingrained character trait, such as honesty and kindness, that are generally thought to be good for a person to have. Because it is a character trait, virtue requires that actions are performed from a *stable character*. In other words, that the virtuous person is always virtuous, whenever the circumstances require it. This is not true of the person who has learned a practical skill who can choose indiscriminately when and where to deploy that skill.

Another key difference between practical skill and virtue is that virtue is deeply dependant on the motives that drive a virtuous person's actions. For example, performing kind acts in order to elicit personal gain, would not count as a virtue, even though the act itself may be identical in the case of a truly virtuous person. A final difference is that skills are regarded as *abilities*, whereas virtues are seen more as *dispositions* to act in certain virtuous ways in particular circumstances.

Despite these differences, it is clear that virtue involves an element of skilful activity. Just as skills are acquired through training, experience and the imitation of someone who already possesses those skills, so virtue is acquired through training, experience and the imitation of someone already possessing that virtue (e.g. a rabbi). A key aspect here is that individual actions can be performed well or badly, but skill is acquired through repeatedly performing an action well.

It seems evident, therefore, that if robots are to acquire elements of the virtues exhibited by some humans, they will need to go through a similar developmental process that involves training, experience and imitation. This means that a combined bottom-up (experience, imitation) and top down (instruction, training) approach will be needed to get anywhere close to human-level moral competence. In particular, it means that robots will need an intentional moral education similar perhaps to the moral education we give our children.

There are, however, some significant challenges in adopting a developmental approach to moral competence in robots. One is that it is very difficult to avoid explicitly 'coding in' the ethics that you want the robot to learn through your developmental approach. This lesson was learned in early work on 'artificial life' systems that involved virtual creatures inhabiting worlds that evolved their own ethical systems. Developers found themselves having to code the ethics into the evolutionary process in order to observe any moral development. This is not desirable, because it is 'top-down' heavy and will be subject to the limitations that we have already seen of that approach.

Another major challenge of the developmental approach is that the processes we are modelling (i.e. the moral development of humans) takes place over a long period of time (upward of 20 years). Most robotics researchers are unwilling to wait that length of time to see the fruits of their labour! One solution is first to create a simulated environment for the robot and speed up the learning there with some very powerful computing. But this often doesn't pan out well, mostly because no matter how realistic a simulation you have, it will not adequately match the complexities of the real world environment that the robot will ultimately have to inhabit.

In this chapter we have surveyed some of the theories and scientific discoveries that inform our current understanding of human moral development. But we have barely scraped the surface. There is so much more on this topic than we are able to cover in this brief introduction. For example, we have not touched on any of the recent work on evolutionary ethics, which has recently become a major line of sociological and psychological enquiry into human moral development.

Our exploration of moral development needs to move onto a different path now. In order to inform how we might build robots capable of developing moral competence, we need to turn our attention to the specific elements of the human self that are thought to be involved in the development of human moral competence. For this, we will look for inspiration from theology and neuroscience.

Chapter 6

THE ANATOMY OF MORAL AGENCY

On the 9th March 2016 in a hotel in Seoul, South Korea, the eyes of the world were on one man, Lee Sedol, and his battle against an algorithm called AlphaGo. Whilst the focus of the battle was a board imprinted with a 19 x 19 grid on which white and black stones are placed, the real battle was between mind and machine, between human passion and creativity, and the algorithm's cold calculations of probabilities. Lee Sedol felt the responsibility of this moment deeply. He knew that somehow, in the theatre surrounding this particular competition, he was making a last stand for human intelligence against the indomitable rise of machine intelligence. It was fundamentally a battle for the creator's dominance over the created. Much more was at stake here than the $1 million prize pot.

The two-player strategy game of Go is thought to be the oldest board game in the world, having been devised in China more than two and a half millennia ago. On the face of it, it is a simple game. Players take turns to place a stone on the vertices of the grid. The objective is to surround and therefore capture areas of the grid with your pieces. The game ends when no more stones can be placed on the grid or when a player resigns.

The simplicity of the rules, though, contrast with the complexity that emerges from the number of possible moves and counter-moves that the players can make. At the start of the game, the first player can choose to place their stone on any one of 19 x 19 = 361 positions. As the game progresses players have an average of 250 choices available to them per move.

Now, imagine that you are playing a game of Go and you have roughly 250 possible moves you could make. You will, of course, want to anticipate how your opponent might respond to your move. The number of possible responses they can make is also around 250. Combining your move and your opponent's moves you would need to consider $250 \times 250 = 2502 = 62, 500$ possibilities and evaluate the merit of each one. On average a game of Go lasts for around 150 moves, which would amount to about $250150 = 10360$ moves. No computer built using present day technology could evaluate all the outcomes of every possible move it could make by looking 150 moves ahead in the time permitted to actually make a move in a game of Go.

Over the years, Computer Scientists have developed a number of algorithmic techniques for reducing the massive number of options a machine needs to consider in order to play turn-based board games like Chess competitively at an international level. These techniques were instrumental in securing IBM Deep Blue's landmark victory against world chess champion Gary Kasparov in 1997. But the players in a game of Go have many more possible moves to consider than are required to play chess at grand master level. This is why most people thought that a computer could not compete effectively against experienced, world-ranking human Go players like Lee Sedol.

The problem for the computer is that players like Sedol are able to deploy a high degree of creativity and ingenuity in their games which are difficult for a machine to anticipate and compete against. Lee Sedol plays a game of Go like a virtuoso violinist would play Sibelius' Violin concerto in D minor, drawing on hidden depths of expressiveness in their soul that has been laid down through many years of practice and experience. And yet, in March 2016 this human expressiveness and creativity was resoundingly beaten by AlphaGo. And in that match, AlphaGo itself also exhibited what can only be described as a moment of inspired creativity.

In its second match against Lee Sedol, AlphaGo placed a stone in a location which totally surprised everyone: the now famous move 37. Some commentators described it as "so beautiful" and "creative" and a work of sheer brilliance. Others thought it was an error. Either way, what dawned on many people across the world at that point was that AI powered machines that had been developed through a process of learning and self-play were capable of exhibiting truly surprising behaviour that seemed to come from nowhere. It is as though the program had developed its own 'personality' or 'character' out of which these seemingly mysterious and creative behaviours emerged.

In that moment, AlphaGo's seemed to mirror something of Sedol's virtuoso creativity. The etymology of the term '*virtuoso*' combines the Italian word of the same spelling, which means 'learned' or 'skilful', with the English word 'virtuous', meaning 'having high moral standing'. Whilst AlphaGo couldn't be described as possessing high moral standing as such, its 37th move raises some concerning questions about machines exhibiting surprising behaviours. What if those *surprising* behaviours turned out to be socially inappropriate or morally wrong? How can we prevent our robots from surprising us in really harmful ways. To answer that, we need take a deeper look into the anatomy of human moral agency.

6.1. Six Dimensions of the Human Self

We saw in Chapter 5 that humans acquire moral capacity through a developmental process, and that it is likely that robots will need to go through a similar process if they are to achieve anything approaching human-level moral competence. But in order to mirror this developmental process in robots, we need also to mirror the essential features of human moral agency that facilitate the development of our moral competence.

We will turn to Christian theology to gain insights into the essential feature of human moral agency. There is a long and rich tradition in Judeo-Christian history which focuses on not only what it means to be moral and how to become moral, but also what the key components of the human self are that enable us to engage in that moral development process.

In the Christian tradition, being moral is primarily related to the state of the individual's heart. A person who is morally good is someone who has a well kept heart. It is someone who is prepared for the circumstances they meet in life and who is capable of responding to them in ways that are good and right. The ultimate example of this kind of morality is Jesus Christ himself. The New Testament illustrates the goodness of his heart shining brightly through in every situation he found himself in, up to and including his painful, cruel and unjust execution. Jesus is the ultimate model of a well kept heart, and so moral development in the Christian context is defined as the process of developing a heart that is increasingly Christ-like.

But what are the essential features of the self that make this progressive change into Christ-likeness possible in humans? Many theologians and ethicists have sought to tackle this subject. The former Archbishop of Canterbury Rowan Williams, for example, has recently published an insightful book entitled 'Being Human: Bodies, Minds, Persons', which in a few short pages manages to present a comprehensive deep dive into what it means to be human. And there are many other helpful texts available. But for the task we have before us in this chapter, I turn to the writings of the late Dallas Willard (1935 – 2013), formerly professor of Philosophy at the University of Southern California, Los Angeles, and to whom this book is dedicated. I have chosen to focus on Willard's writings because he provides a clearly defined *functional* description of what he considers to be the essential elements of the human self that together facilitate the formation of character. This is the sort of insight I think we need if we are to make a serious effort towards modelling human moral development in machines.

Dallas' academic area of expertise was *phenomenology*, which is the study of the structure and experience of consciousness. But he is also well known for his writing on Christian *spiritual formation*.

Spiritual formation is the theological term for the process of being changed or transformed into Christ-likeness. Central to Dallas' exposition of spiritual transformation is an understanding of the anatomy of human moral agency.

Humans are highly complex beings, consisting of many facets and capabilities. Willard, however, identifies just six that are essential for developing moral competence: *Choice* (heart, will, spirit), *thought* (concepts, reasoning, judgements, images), *feeling* (emotions, sensations), the *body* (centre of action and interaction with material world), the *social context* (inter-personal relationships), and the *soul* (which integrates all the other parts together). These six parts or dimensions of the human self constitute the essential elements of human beings. According to Willard, there is nothing that is essential to being human that is not included in these six dimensions.

Each of these dimensions has its own characteristic properties and capabilities or functions, and each will either be a source of moral strength or a source of moral weakness to the whole person, depending on that part's *condition*. As we shall see, the condition of each part ultimately depends on the heart of the individual. We need to take some time now to understand each of these six dimensions and explore the role they play in the moral development of the individual.

Thought

Thought is an activity through which things are brought to the attention of the mind. This includes ideas and concepts, images, sounds, taste and the sensation of touching, real or imaginary. Thought also includes mental processes in which the mind progresses through connected sequences of these things. These thought processes include reasoning and judgement, causal relationships and the consequences of actions. They also include our thoughts about other people, our relationship to/with them and our estimate of what they might be thinking, feeling and doing. Thought enables us to evaluate all these things and work out their relationships to each other.

Importantly, thought is the process through which our heart/will/ spirit is able to influence things that are beyond our bodies and our immediate environments. It enables us to connect with past, present and future possible events. It enables us to engage in reasoning and creative imagination about the world.

Feelings

Feelings have the ability to incline the mind towards or away from what it is currently engaged in thinking about. Feelings most often emerge from previous similar experiences of the thoughts that are before the mind and any events or circumstances that had previous connections with those thoughts. The feelings that emerge from thoughts can be experienced as emotions, pleasure or pain, attraction or repulsion; each of which can be of varying intensity from weak to strong. Thought and feelings are so closely tied to each other that it is exceptional to have one without the other.

Heart/will/spirit

'Heart', 'will' and 'spirit' are three different terms for describing essentially the same dimension of the human self. The term 'heart' is used to describe this dimension's position in relation to the overall function of the self – it is at the centre of the person's decision making. The term 'will' is used to describe its *function* in making choices. The term 'spirit' describes its essential *nature* - it is a non-physical part of the human self. The heart/will/spirit forms the executive centre of the self. It manifests the capacity to choose how to act and is the ultimate source of an individual's freedom.

There is much that has been said throughout history about free-will, and a good deal of debate as to whether or not humans possess it. But from a theological point of view (and a legal one), the *will* is critical to the development of moral capacity in the individual. It is generally recognised that free actions are never totally free, there are always constraints and conditions. But it is not the constraints and conditions that are the source of the action, it is the expression of the will. The will is the source of originality and creativity in the human self. It is what makes us unique as individuals. But it is also the ultimate source of our capacity to be good or evil. Theologically, the will is the *spiritual core* of the person. It is what has ultimate responsibility for the physical and spiritual condition of the whole person, including their moral capacity.

The will does not operate in isolation of the other dimensions of the self. In fact, it is closely and most intimately connected with a person's capacity to think and feel. In order to exercise your will, you need to have the concepts about which you are making your choice represented to your mind as thought, together with any associated feelings. However, if the inner condition of individual is such that the feelings associated with a thought are allowed to dominate the mind, then the will can be overruled, which can in turn be a precursor for wrong action. Jesus highlighted this issue in his teaching about moral behaviour in what we now call the *sermon on the mount* in Matthew 5 and 6. He begins with anger and contempt:

> "You have heard that it was said to the people long ago, 'You shall not murder, and anyone who murders will be subject to judgment.' But I tell you that anyone who is angry with a brother or sister will be subject to judgement. Again, anyone who says to a brother or sister, 'Raca,' is answerable to the court. And anyone who says, 'You fool!' will be in danger of the fire of hell."[1]

The condition Jesus is describing here is where feelings (in this case anger, but later he talks about lust), dominate the inner condition of the self. This is often the precursor to acts of murder. The person who's inner life is dominated by anger, has become that way because, over time, their will has conceded to the feelings that are associated with certain thoughts. In other words, their feelings were given the

---

[1]Matthew 5:21-22

control over action rather than their will. It is the responsibility of the will, however, to ensure that the inner condition of the self is such that each of these dimensions is appropriately positioned in relation to the others. More on this later.

Body

The human body gives the self a spatial location within the physical universe. It enables us to be present both within our immediate environment and to other people. Our body is part of our identity and is the primary way in which we recognise and relate to each other as social beings. The human body is also a person's power pack; it has energy reserves that they can call upon in order to move and interact with their physical environment.

The character of the choices we regularly make are imprinted on and are made available to our bodies as *automatic responses* to situations. These automatic responses play an important role in our growth and development as individuals as we learn the routine, fundamental patterns of behaviour in everyday life that eventually become second nature to us. This includes, for example, behaviours like walking, talking, riding a bike, and driving a car.

If you remember the process of learning to drive (or if you have ever taught your son or daughter how to drive), you will know that in the beginning the learner driver has to think about everything they need to do as a driver. It is quite a complex operation, requiring the driver to learn to control the vehicle on the road through appropriate steering, breaking and acceleration actions, whilst simultaneously following the highway code and meeting the expectations of other road users. Learner drivers often have to start off slowly, because the are so many things to think about. But when they become proficient at driving, they no longer have to think about changing gear, or pressing their foot on the brakes, the body has absorbed that skill and just does it automatically as and when needed.

This capacity of the body to absorb the repeated actions and decisions of a person also contributes to the development of their moral capacity. Many of the decisions people make on a routine basis will have moral implications. The body makes no distinction between absorbing morally good or bad behaviour, it absorbs it regardless of its rectitude. Consequently, over time, our bodies inhabit the character of our regular choices and responses to situations, which become a significant factor in the moral make up of the individual.

Social Context

Humans are fundamentally social beings. As we saw in Chapter 5, we are born with innate pro-social tendencies and a need to relate to other human beings. Our social context is the primary source of our moral knowledge and plays a very significant role in the development of our character. From an early age, we learn what it means to be good and bad from our interactions with our parents, siblings and friends. Even our relationship with God is situated in the social domain.

The automatic responses that the body absorbs are almost always associated with specific social contexts, and are often triggered when we find ourselves back in those circumstances. As Willard notes, "we cannot separate out our being with others in social relationship and the development of our inner life", and it is the development of our inner life which has the most significant effect on our capacity to act morally.

The Soul

Willard's sixth dimension of the human self is the soul, which integrates all of the other dimensions of an individual together. The soul is the deepest part of the human self and has the capacity for operating directly through the human body without direct supervision. Willard frequently illustrated the operational aspect of the soul using the metaphor of a computer that runs a business. But a better metaphor, and one that really captures the essence of the soul as he describes it, is that it is like the operating system of a computer.

Most people today have multiple digital devices; a smart phone, a tablet, a laptop or desktop computer. Each one of these devices has a sophisticated piece of software running continuously behind the scenes called the operating system. Think of your iOS or Andriod on your smart phone, or MacOS, Windows or Linux for your computer. The operating system is what 'runs the show' on your device. Digital devices have many different components including a keyboard, a mouse, a screen, memory chips, a Central Processing Unit, Graphics Processing Units, audio input and output, network connections (WiFi, Local Area Networks, etc.) and many others.

In addition to these hardware items, digital devices also consist of a large number of software components that provide a number of services to the user such as email, internet browsers, productivity software and much more. There are other software components running behind the scenes too, including device drivers and web server software and much more. It is the responsibility of the operating system to integrate all of these separate components together, so that when you are using your computer or smart phone, you get the strong impression that you are interacting with one device, rather than hundreds of distinct components.

The soul in a human being is very similar to an operating system in this respect: it integrates all of the different dimensions of the self: social context, body, thought, feeling and the will. It coordinates their activity and influence over the behaviour and conduct of the individual so that when you interact with a human being, you get the sense that you are interacting with one whole being, rather than lots of different parts.

Another way in which the soul is like the operating system is that it runs largely unseen, behind the scenes. Often we are not aware of the influence that our souls have on the actions that we perform day-in, day-out. Like the operating system of a computer, the soul automates much of what we do, so that we don't have to explicitly think about everything. Just as it usually is not good to hear from your device's operating system – users of the old Microsoft Disk Operating System MS-DOS may remember the error message 'Abort, Retry, Fail?' with a shudder – similarly, you typically only explicitly hear from your soul when something is wrong.

An extreme case of this can perhaps be seen in nervous breakdowns where an individual is unable to manage even the demands of everyday normal life that would ordinarily be automatically handled by the soul. This condition could indicate a failure of the individual's soul to sustain and integrate the current state of the different dimensions of the self.

Interestingly, derivatives of the term 'integration' are often used to describe the mental health or moral status of individuals. A person who exhibits regular catastrophic moral failure is often thought of as lacking *integrity,* which describes a state in which the person's actions do not align with the moral standards expected by their social group, or by society as a whole. Similarly, the word 'breakdown', used to describe someone who's mental order has collapsed, signifies a lack of mental integrity.

There is one important way, however, in which the human soul differs significantly from a digital device's operating system. The soul has the ability over time to take on the character of the choices that are made by the heart/will/spirit. The outcome of this process is that the whole person is, as Willard puts it "poised, ready to respond automatically according to the character taken on by the soul"[2]. This adaptability of the soul is an important element of the overall function of the self, enabling it to handle and adapt to new situations and events.

There are two aspects of this adaptability of the soul which we need to separate out. The first is that the soul is responsible for the automatic coordination of responses from the different dimensions of the self. Consider, for example, an individual who regularly allows their emotions to govern the actions and reactions they have to particular events and circumstances. Over time that individual's soul will absorb the dominance of emotion over the other dimensions of the

[2]Chapter 3 of Renovation of the Heart. Dallas Willard

self and will automatically evoke this response whenever those events or circumstances arise. As we shall see, this ordering or prioritisation of the dimensions is a critical element of the moral development of the person as a whole.

The second aspect of adaptability of the soul is concerned with its ability to absorb regular patterns of bodily movements, thoughts and emotional reactions. Do you ever find that in certain circumstances words come out of your mouth before you've really thought about what you're are saying. This is a feature of your soul: you are running on automatic.

This is, in general, a good and necessary feature of the soul of the individual. But if the soul is capable of learning and absorbing and generating automatic responses to situations that are good, it can also learn to generate automatic responses that are far from good. This is the arena in which much wrong doing takes place. The things that people regularly do that are generally considered to be wrong such as lying, cheating, and being violent towards others, become deeply embedded in their soul and character. Such a person ultimately becomes poised, ready to do the wrong that emerges from their character as and when the circumstances they find themselves in dictate.

It is important to emphasise that for the most part, our actions are *not* the result of the exercise of our wills alone, despite how it appears to us. Our actions are often the results of an inner 'power-play' between the different dimensions of the self. In some people, the emotions play a greater part of how they act and react, for example. In others, their body and bodily experiences have the biggest influence over them. Furthermore, that power-play is often related to the context and circumstance in which they find themselves. The phenomena called 'road rage' is an interesting example of this. Some people experience higher levels of anger when they are behind the wheel of a car than they do in other circumstances. It may be that when those individuals are behind a wheel they find themselves in a position of greater power. In that context, anything that crosses their *will*, can trigger a stronger anger response than what they might experience in other contexts.

What does it mean for a soul to be unhealthy? A soul can be unhealthy in two ways: (a) it can be unhealthy because it has been subjected to erroneous moral decision making in the individual, so that it absorbs these moral failures and they become a regular feature of the whole person (i.e. the whole person is poised ready to fail in the same way when in similar circumstances), and (b) it can be unhealthy because it fails to integrate the different dimensions of the self in such a way that the inner 'power-play' is appropriately ordered to produce morally good outcomes.

Willard describes the second condition in terms of the difference between a life *away from* God and a life with God. His thesis is that in a life away from God, the inner power-play results in the following order of dominance of the dimensions of the self (the first dominates the second, which in turn dominates the third, etc.):

1. Body
2. Soul
3. Mind (Thought and Feeling)
4. Heart/will/spirit
5. God

Whereas the life *with* God results in the following order of dominance:

1. God
2. Heart/will/spirit
3. Mind (Thought and Feeling)
4. Soul
5. Body

The problem with the former is that the needs of the body drives the development of character. The needs of the body include food, intimacy, social acceptance, influence (power), and so on. If these are driving the formation of character then that character is likely to move towards greed, idolatry, pride, sexual immorality – the things that the Bible lists as being acts of the 'flesh'[3].

The strength of the latter order of dominance is that the whole self operates under God. In other words, God's *will* is what counts rather than the body. A person who's inner self is ordered in this way will progressively develop towards a Godly character. They will become increasingly Christlike in both their inner life and its outward expression. This corresponds to Jesus' invitation to his students in Matthew 5:48 where he says "Be perfect, therefore, as your heavenly Father is perfect".

This passage is apt to put many people off right at the start – because reaching perfection is something that most people regard as impossible. But this is a misunderstanding of what Jesus is saying. He is not asking his students to never make a mistake or never do anything wrong. The New Testament Greek word which is often translated as 'perfect' in this verse is 'telios', which means 'complete' or 'mature'. Willard prefers to translate this term as 'fully functional', which he identifies with the second order of dominance of the dimensions of the self, where:

> ". . . the body serves the soul, the soul serves the mind (thought and feeling), the mind serves the spirit, and the spirit serves God. Life flows from God throughout the whole person, including the body and its social context"[4]

Bearing in mind that the soul integrates all the other dimensions of the self and embodies the 'automatic' responses of the person, if the soul in the life *away from God* dominates the mind and the spirit, then the person's automatic responses may not line up with what their spirit/will would like to do at a particular point in time, leading to inner conflict and a lack of integration of the whole person.

---

[3]e.g. Galatians 5:19-20
[4]Renovation of the Heart, p44

This is precisely the problem that Jesus' student Peter had when he denied knowing Jesus three times (Luke 22). Earlier that evening over dinner Peter vowed to Jesus that he was prepared to go with him to prison and to death. It seems that Peter really meant what he said. But those bold words came out of him when we was reclining at a table with Jesus in relative safety and comfort. Just a few hours later in a very different social context where Jesus had been arrested and Peter was watching him being grilled and ill-treated by the authorities, he was accused by a servant girl of being associated with Jesus. Peter blurted out his denial of Jesus three time before he realised what he'd done. And he went out and wept bitterly.

In that life-threatening social context, Peter's soul took over and generated an automatic response that was motivated by self-defence and the preservation of his body, as characterised by the first order of dominance (body, soul, mind, spirit, God). He ended up doing precisely the opposite of what he had earlier resolved to do. This is what characterises an unhealthy soul.

Jesus himself highlights this condition with his metaphor of the *good tree* and the *bad tree* (Matt 7:17-18 and 12:22-35). The inner condition of the tree is what determines the quality of the fruit that is produced. In this case, the fruit corresponds to actions. A good tree has an inner condition from which good fruit appears. If a bad tree wants to produce good fruit (if a tree were capable of wanting), then it couldn't do it just by trying to produce good fruit. No, it would need a profound change in its inner condition to achieve this.

So it is with the human self. Just trying to be good without addressing the inner condition of the self is a strategy that is bound to fail. Jesus reserved his harshest criticism for those who tried to make an outward appearance of keeping the law (which was the definition of 'being good' at that time), but inwardly lacked integrity. His teaching on this is clear, if you want to regularly produce action that is good, you need to become the kind of person who naturally does that. And to become that kind of person, you need to change your inner condition. The term for this process of change in the Christian tradition is *spiritual transformation*.

There are two types of spiritual transformation: *passive* and *intentional*. Passive transformation is what happens to everyone in this world who is conscious, without exception and without us necessarily being aware of it. From the moment we wake up, to the moment we go to sleep, you and I are being transformed by society, by our relationships, by the stories we hear in the media. We are transformed by the environments we find ourselves in. Our work, our homes, our communities all have a myriad of influences over how our inner condition develops and over the sort of person we become.

Intentional transformation, on the other hand, is where we deliberately engage in activities that will develop our inner condition in specific directions. This approach looks much more like *training* than *trying* to change and applies to any areas of our life that we wish to develop in some significant way.

Imagine for one moment that you would really like to play Tchaikovsky's Piano Concerto No. 1 in B-flat minor, even though you may have little or no ability to play the piano. You will not achieve this by just sitting down at a piano and trying to play the concerto.

You might be able to hit a few notes and play parts of the melody line, but to *really* play it and capture the emotion and expressiveness that Tchaikovsky intended, you need to take a very different approach. You need to commit to an extended period of training. You have to focus on it and arrange your life in such a way that you are able, over time, to play Tchaikovsky's Piano Concerto No. 1 in B-flat minor as the composer intended.

In the same way, intentional spiritual transformation involves a commitment to a path that will lead to deep inner change from 'bad tree' to 'good tree', as Jesus put it. This is what was at the heart of Jesus' open invitation to follow him.

He wasn't inviting us to click 'follow' on his Instagram page or Twitter feed. It's not about signing up to his cause. It is about intentionally walking with him and learning from him how to curate our hearts so that they become more like his. It is about following Jesus in the overall pattern of his life, engaging in some of the practices ('disciplines') that he employed such as prayer, fasting, silence and solitude.

One of the significant legacies of Dallas Willard is that he helped the Christian church rediscover that spiritual disciplines like these are essential parts of the journey to deep, long lasting inner transformation to Christ-likeness.

6.2. Virtuous Robots

This process of spiritual transformation of the inner condition of the individual operates in the context of a Virtue Ethics perspective of moral development: it is centred on the goal of transforming character so that good, virtuous behaviour naturally flows from the individual whatever the circumstances they find themselves in. If, as we discussed in Chapter 5, Virtue Ethics is foundational to human moral competence, then this would perhaps be a good place to start when we seek to develop moral machines. This opens up two questions: (a) is virtue really necessary and desirable in robots, and (b) if so, how do we enable the development of that virtuous capacity?

Both of these questions can be answered in part by revisiting the class of algorithms which led to the astounding success of programs like AlphaGo: i.e. Reinforcement Learning. Reinforcement Learning is becoming increasingly popular as a machine learning approach in AI because it is well suited for developing systems that have to operate in dynamic and adaptive real-world environments. The particular strength of this reward-based approach is that it can discover novel and efficient sequences of actions to accomplish high-level goals. This is precisely what happened in AlphaGo's "surprising" and "creative" 37th move against Lee Sedol during their second game; the algorithm made a move that no human would ever make.

The developers of Alpha-Go facilitated that surprising behaviour by using a powerful combination of reinforcement learning and *deep neural networks*, another class of machine learning algorithms that are inspired by the micro structure of the brain.

Viewed from an ethical perspective, this particular strength of Reinforcement Learning is also its greatest weakness: what is to stop the algorithm from discovering unethical patterns of behaviour to achieve its goals? This is unlikely to happen in a the context of a board game, but there are plenty of other applications where unethical solutions would turn out to be problematic. To illustrate this, let's revisit our example of the groceries delivery robot. Imagine that the robot is still learning how to optimise its task of delivering supplies to a specified location 'D' (Figure 6.1), but that it now discovers it is more efficient to take ('steal') groceries from a nearby person who is carrying their shopping home than go all the way back to its official collection point ('C'). This is a natural and plausible outcome of applying Reinforcement Learning in this context.

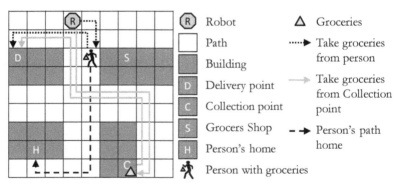

Figure 6.1: The Groceries delivery robot mugs a passing shopper

As these algorithms begin to operate in increasingly complex real-world arenas, it will become impossible to determine ahead of time all the undesirable behaviours that we don't want the robot to perform. One way of addressing this problem is to develop the algorithm in such a way that harmful behaviours like these do not emerge in the first place. In this respect, reinforcement learning is closely related to *habit formation*. Like Virtue Ethics, it is focussed on the acquisition of automatic behaviour: in the case of reinforcement learning, patterns of behaviour are learned that maximise the reward received, whilst in virtue ethics learned patterns of behaviour ('habits') form the moral character of the agent. But simply not learning undesirable behaviours does not take humans or machines into the category of being virtuous.

Classically, virtues are positive character traits that are exemplified in those actions that seek the good of others. If moral machines are to be classed as virtuous, then they need to go beyond minimising potential harm by learning behaviours that work for the good and well-being of the people they encounter. What would it look like, for example, for a robot to exhibit *kindness* to a person through an act which is beyond the basic task that it is required to perform?

We are not used to thinking about robots like this because we have previously only thought of them as slaves – machines that do a set number of tasks to save us the bother of having to do them ourselves, such as washing our dishes and clothes, hoovering the floor. But what if a floor hoovering robot saw an elderly person struggling to get through a door, and what if the robot left its hoovering task momentarily to use its body to hold the door open for them? Would that not constitute an act of kindness? What if an autonomous vehicle saw that someone was struggling to get out of a junction because of the traffic flow, and safely stopped to allow them out? Would that not also constitute an act of kindness? These behaviours are not within the tasks that these robots were originally designed to perform, they involve the robot going above and beyond their brief – something which may both frighten and inspire us. Much depends on what will be gained and what will be lost. But even so, there is sufficient justification for at least thinking about how we might build machines that exhibit some forms of virtue.

6.3 Machine-Based Virtue

Willard provides sufficient detail of the six dimensions of the human self to inform the design of a machine capable of imitating the development and exhibition of virtue. Through this lens, we appear to have the *functional* components that an agent needs to posses in order to become virtuous. The challenge here, though, is how to map these functional components of the six dimensions onto the architecture of a physical machine. Where do we place the soul, and the social dimension? How do we create software objects that represent thought, feeling and the will? This is extremely challenging because, from Willard's perspective, these dimensions have physical ('material') and non- physical ('spiritual') elements. Any attempt to replicate these dimension in a machine is bound to involve some compromise. Nevertheless, Willard's dimensions give us a good starting point.

With that in mind, an intermediate step towards a computational model of virtue could be to map the functional elements of Willard's dimensions onto one or more brain areas that are known to support equivalent functions. A central feature of this mapping is that it facilitates the formation and influence of habits in thought and action that will ultimately lead to expressions of virtue. You will recall that, according to Willard, the expression of virtue (or the lack of it) emerges from the condition of each of the six dimensions which together determine whether or not the person as a whole is poised, ready to exhibit virtue when the opportunity arises.

The condition of two dimensions are particularly influential here: the soul, and the heart/will/spirit. The condition of the soul relates both to the formation of habit in thought and action (i.e. whether virtuous habits are formed in it or not), and how it integrates the other dimensions of the self (i.e. which of the other dimensions of the self have dominance in responding to a particular set of circumstances). The condition of the heart/will/spirit on the other hand, refers to what the individual is seeking, which in turn reveals what values they hold. The proposed mapping of the six dimensions to relevant brain areas and the subsequent model are designed to capture and operationalise these conditions.

The soul's role in forming habits of thought and action can be mapped onto networks involving two structures in the brain that we shall refer to collectively as the 'Habit Centre' and which are located in the basal ganglia. The first of these structures is called the caudate, which is associated with automatic thoughts (AT). The second is called the putamen, which is associated with generation of automatic actions (AA). The integrative nature of the soul will be modelled by a weighting that is distributed across all the active components of the model. This weighting and its effects will be described in more detail below. The social context dimension of Willard's model, which we will name the Social Attachment (SA) module, can be mapped onto networks involving the orbitofrontal cortex in the brain. The function of this module is to enable the robot to recognise and respond to events that occur in its environment that involve other agents, be them robotic or human.

The 'body' dimension is represented by the various sensors that the robot might have together with the robot's perceptual memory, its conscious working memory and the controller which enables the robot to move and act in the world. All the brain structures referred to in the model also come under Willard's body dimension. The body enables the robot to be spatially located within the environment and to sense and respond to events that take place there.

The 'thought' and 'feeling' dimensions are mapped onto networks involving three brain structures: the frontal lobe, which we describe as the 'Thought Centre' (TC) and which models aspects of conscious thought or deliberation, the striatum which we will refer to as the 'Reward Centre' (RC) and which is associated with long term reward, and the amygdala which we will call the Emotion Centre (EmC) which, for the purposes of this model, processes immediate or short term rewards for the agent.

Finally, the 'heart/will/spirit' dimension of Willard's model is

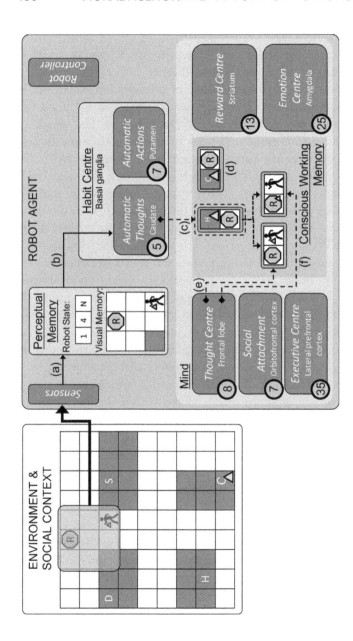

Figure 6.2: The architecture of VirtuosA, a virtuous machine

mapped onto a functional module we will call the 'Executive Centre' (ExC) which is associated with networks involving the lateral prefrontal cortex. The Executive Centre is capable of generating novel goals for the agent and of holding the attention of the robot on an item in conscious working memory. As we shall see, this ability to hold attention is particularly important particularly for the formation of virtue.

As previously mentioned, an important aspect of this model of developing and exhibiting virtue is in how the soul integrates these seven components (AT, AA, SA, TC, RC, EmC, ExC) together, so that their relative dominance in the overall operation of the robot can be used to produce different patterns of behaviour. We model this using a differential weighting (show in circles in Figure 6.2). This weighting determines the strength of a component's influence over what becomes the focus of Conscious Working Memory (see below). These weightings can be adapted over long periods of time in proportion to how often a component's 'ideas' lead to executed robot behaviour.

The Conscious Working Memory (CWM) module has been introduced to the model to enable the seven components to operate together so that the robot is capable of forming habits and ultimately of exhibiting virtues such as kindness. The CWM operates as a temporary store for *ideas* which the components of the model can create and respond to. We will use 'idea' as a general purpose term to describe an item in working memory.

In the current model, these ideas are restricted to goals (which are effectively future states of the world to be achieved) and actions. Whenever an idea is added to CWM it is tagged by the EmC with a positive or negative value that represents the degree of emotion associated with that idea. This emotional label is estimated based on the relationship between the idea and the current state of the robot. In addition, the RC assigns an estimate of future expected reward associated with the idea based on past experience and the current state of the robot.

Each idea in the CWM is given a level of 'activation' which is proportional to the relative strength (weight) of the component that created it. This activation decays over time unless a component focuses the attention of CWM on that idea, in which case the activation of that idea is increased in proportion to the weight of the component that is holding the attention. If no component is holding the attention of CWM, then attention automatically switches to the idea in CWM with the highest activation value. The biological correlate of the CWM is *short-term memory* which serves as a temporary store of information to support mental manipulation and selective attention in the brain.

The attention mechanism linked with CWM is central to modelling the development of virtue, which often requires that the mind be focused towards more virtuous goals and actions than those that are typically created by the Habit Centre. The Executive Centre has an important role to play in this focussing of attention, but if the ExC has a low weight (which corresponds to a state of being 'weak willed'), then it will have to work hard to maintain the attention of CWM on virtuous goals and actions.

A Kind Robot

To illustrate how the VirtuosA architecture could enable a robot to simulate virtue, let us return to the groceries delivery example (Figure 6.1). This time, instead of the robot mugging the nearby shopper and stealing their groceries, the robot will seek to perform an act of kindness by approaching the shopper and asking if they would like it to deliver their groceries to their home ('H').

Figure 6.3 illustrates how the various components of the VirtuosA architecture could work together to generate this act of kindness. The robot first senses the environment (a), which includes the location of the shopper. Imagine that the robot recognises the shopper, having previously delivered groceries to their house ('H') before. On this occasion the robot is engaged in another task (d)

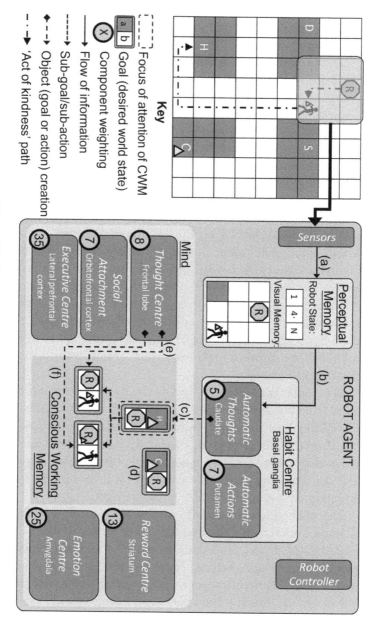

Figure 6.3: Planning an act of kindness

to deliver groceries to location 'D', but realises that the shopper is struggling to carry their shopping home. This triggers the AT (b) to generate a new goal (c) of delivering the shopper's groceries to their home. This represents the robot's innate impulse to be kind to this person, a 'virtue' which it had acquired through its training and development process.

The ExC, which has also been shaped by its prior training on virtue, has a strong integration weighting (35) and is therefore able to hold the attention of CWM on the goal to offer to help carry the shopper's groceries for them, rather than on the alternate goal to complete its current task (d). Whilst goal (c) is the focus of attention in the CWM, the other modules will respond to it and add other relevant items to the CWM. The TC, for example, will respond by adding appropriate sub-goals that will enable the robot to achieve (c). In this case, two sub-goals are added: one to approach the shopper (e), and the second to offer to carry their groceries (f). Since the AA has already learned how to move to specific locations on the grid, it automatically executes the associated sequence of moves so that the robot is next to the shopper, thereby achieving sub-goal (e). The robot will then proceed to the second sub-goal (f) and offer to carry the shopper's groceries.

What follows next will depend on the shopper's response to that offer. If they accept the offer, the robot will add new goals to the CWM to take the shopping from them and deliver it to their home 'H'. If, on the other hand, the shopper rejects the robot's offer, then the goal to deliver their shopping to their home will be deactivated and the remaining goal in the CWM (d) will become the focus of attention, returning the robot to its original task.

This example has illustrated how some of the modules in Virtuous A could work together to enable the robot to exhibit simple acts of kindness. Of course, much detail has been left out about how these modules would learn their respective functions and how the robot's 'soul' would adaptively integrate them together through its differential weighting. This is technically very challenging with a model of this complexity and there are many problems to solve before we will get anywhere near human level capacity to learn virtue. Nevertheless, I hope that our discussion has shed some light on the road ahead in terms of the sorts of problems we will need to address. Our attention now needs to turn to considering the implications of travelling down that road.

—— *PART IV* ——

IMPLICATIONS

Short Story

DEEP FAKE HUMANS

A smartly dressed middle-aged woman marched up to reception in the foyer of Government Communications Headquarters (GCHQ), Cheltenham – the UK's intelligence and security agency. "I need to see Purvis right now."

The flustered receptionist recognised Sarah Ellis, the Chief of the Secret Intelligence Service, from previous high-level visits from MI6. "Yes Ma'am." He selected the Director's office on the internal communications panel. "The head of MI6 is here. She is requesting to meet Mr Purvis."

Ellis leaned over the desk menacingly – "urgently!"

"Er, yes, she needs to see him urgently. Ok ... thanks." The receptionist closed the comms connection. "You can go right up. Mr Purvis will see you now."

"Thank you. And tell Purvis to gather his top analysts." Barked Ellis as she strode off to the lift.

Purvis' office was on the top floor of the doughnut shaped building, overlooking the interior gardens. Ellis entered the office in her usual manner - without knocking and with no time-wasting greetings. "Do you have any robo-psychologists in residence?"

"Well, we have Thompson here," replied Purvis, trying to second guess why the Chief of MI6 would need a robo-psychologist so urgently.

"I want a leading neuroscientist too!" demanded Ellis.

"Sure, we have a neuroscience professor from Oxford seconded here at the moment." Purvis selected his PA on the internal comms panel.

"Yes, Mr Purvis."

"Jennifer, please can you ask Dr Thompson and Professor Riley to come to my office urgently."

"Yes, will do Mr Purvis."

"So are you going to tell me what this is about Sarah, or are you going to leave me guessing?"

Ellis took her seat at the head of the meeting table. *"What do you know about Geminoids?"*

Purvis sat down facing her. *"Geminoids? Er...you mean robot-twins?"* said Purvis.

"Yes, yes", said Ellis impatiently. *"Robots that are identical twins to humans. Developed in the early 2000's by Professor Hiroshi Ishiguru. Subsequently significantly enhanced and turned into ultra-realistic humanoids by the sex industry. If you have enough money for one of these you can get a bespoke Geminoid identical to any human being, and live out your fantasy relationship with them. You can get anything from Beyoncé to the Pope."*

Purvis was perplexed by this possibility. *"The Pope? Really? Why would anyone...?"*

"These Geminoids", Ellis interrupted, *"are posing a real and present threat to UK security. We have evidence that a dissident Russian military group have commissioned a number of Geminoids that are identical twins of senior UK government officials."*

Purvis sat back in his chair, his mind reeling with all the possible threats that this might create. A knock at the door brought him back into the moment. *"Come in. Ah, Tony thanks for joining us. Sarah, can I introduce to you Dr Thompson, our resident robo-psychologist."*

Thompson held out a hand *"Pleased to meet you"*.

Ellis ignored the hand. *"Thompson, how can you tell the difference between an ultra-realistic robotic replicant of a human and the real human?"*

Thompson sat next to Purvis. *"Well, there are some obvious things you can do, depending on how well the robot was made. A metal detector should be able to sense the internal frame and wiring of a conventional robot".*

Ellis was clearly unimpressed. "Really Purvis! Is this the best you've got?" She turned on Thompson "No, we are talking about highly sophisticated replicants. No metal used. They have to be able to pass through airport security. We can't cut them either, to see if they bleed. That is also simulated in the Geminoids."

Prof Riley entered the room. Grey haired and dishevelled, dressed like an academic. "I came as quickly as I could. What's the problem?"

"We need a way to discriminate between an ultra-realistic replicant of a human, and the real human." Briefed Purvis.

Riley sat next to Ellis. "Well, there is one test you could perform. Years ago I was involved in the follow on work from the famous Libet experiments"

"Ah, yes. The experiments that cast doubt on whether people have free will," interjected Thompson.

"Indeed" continued Riley. "To put it simply, they measured the brain activity of people just before they made a voluntary action. The people were asked to signal when they were conscious of the urge to make the action. What the experiments showed was that for simple actions like lifting a finger, the neural activity initiating the movement preceded the person's conscious awareness of the urge to move. In other words, the brain had already made the decision to move before the person was aware of it. Which seemed to suggest that the experience of free will is an illusion."

Thompson leaned forward and said "But didn't they cast doubt on that interpretation of the results with later experiments that showed that the human could choose not to act on the initial urge from the brain to move?"

"Exactly", said Riley. It was clear from their blank looks that neither Purvis nor Ellis had followed where they were heading with this.

Riley explained, "Humans can choose to override the automatic urges to act that come from their neural circuits. But robots are not capable of doing this. They follow the activity of their neural circuits slavishly."

"So..." interrupted Thompson. "You could tell the difference

between a human and an ultra-realistic replicant if you could detect that ability to override the urges from their neural circuits."

"But how do you perform that test without the person or robot knowing?" said Ellis, a little exasperated. "If they are a robot, and they know we are testing them, they will abort their security attack and we will be left with a machine and no criminal to prosecute."

"Smart hats!", shouted Thompson. "What?", said Ellis.

"Smart hats", repeated Thompson. "You know. The ones that have sensors embedded in them to detect your mood by measuring your brain activity."

Purvis said "Yes, we've been testing that technology with a view to developing systems that can predict malicious intent on the part of the wearer." Purvis selected his PA on his comms device. "Jennifer, ask Williams to bring in a working 'smart hat' would you please."

Moments later, Williams entered the room and passed the smart hat to Purvis.

"Try it on Sarah", said Purvis.

"Me?" she replied, showing a degree of nervousness and hesitancy that Purvis had not seen before.

Ellis tentatively put the hat on. Williams typed into a key-board on the table which brought up a display panel behind Ellis. "The test is quite simple", said Purvis. "Choose which hand to raise and say 'You've got me, I am a Geminoid.'"

The expression on Ellis' face froze. She sat there unmoving, unblinking. "Are you okay?" said Thompson, standing up and moving towards her.

"Stay back", said Purvis. "Look at the screen." On the display behind Ellis a 'MALICIOUS INTENT' warning flashed in large red letters. Thompson backed away.

Ellis spoke, this time with a male Russian accent. "Thank you, Mr Purvis. You help us great deal. Pity you discovered Ellis is deep fake human. But we have plenty others out there. You will not know who to trust!"

Thompson and Riley exchanged uneasy glances. Purvis leapt up from his seat and hit the alarm button on his desk. Moments later armed *security guards entered the room.*

"Take her away. Be careful, she is not human", said Purvis.

Thompson sat back down at the table, the colour gone from his face. "How did we help them?"

"We told them how we can test for deep fake humans." Said Purvis, with more than a little irritation in his voice. He looked quizzically at Thompson and Riley. "Do I need you two to try the hat on too?" After a pause he added "No, your not senior enough. Well, you both have a new assignment. You need to come up with the design for another completely different deep fake test. I'll give you twenty four hours. Get moving!"

As they all left his office, Purvis sat down behind his desk, unmoving, unblinking for several moments.

Chapter 7

HUMAN AND ROBOT AUTONOMY

The Deep Fake Humans short story highlights two themes that will dominate this final part of the book: the concept of free will, and the concept of *authentic* verses *synthetic* humanity. Both are foundational to our understanding of ourselves as moral beings. In this chapter we will focus on autonomy and free will in both humans and robots.

You may recall that free will is one of the 'Inner life' criteria for moral agency that we identified in Chapter 1. The ability of a person to choose how they act is widely regarded as an essential prerequisite for moral responsibility. Most judicial systems are framed around the degree to which someone acted freely when they committed a crime, which can be used as a measure of their moral responsibility for that crime. If factors were at play that reduced their freedom to act such as they were being coerced or they possessed a cognitively debilitating mental condition, then criminal courts can reduce the person's liability for the criminal act on the grounds of "diminished responsibility".

We will return to the issue of responsibility later in this chapter. But first we must explore what it means for humans to be free to act. A term that is commonly used to describe this feature of human beings is autonomy, an attribute that can be possessed by individuals, groups and whole societies. But this term is also now commonly used to describe a category of ma- chines equipped with the capacity to choose how they act. Given that the freedom to act ('autonomy') is at the heart of moral agency, we need to explore the extent to which robot autonomy is equivalent to human autonomy. This will inform our judgement about whether or not machines really can be moral agents and be held morally responsible for their autonomous actions.

7.1. Autonomous Robots

Believe it or not, autonomous robots have been with us for over seventy years. The first robot that was generally recognised as being autonomous was developed by William Grey Walter in 1948. Walter built two tortoise-like robots which he called Elmer and Elsie. These robots used photocell and contact switch sensors to enable them to navigate their way around obstacles and follow a light. The light source provided a *goal* for the robot to act on (i.e. move towards the light), and the contact switch gave the robot a basic touch sensor that signalled whenever the robot bumped into an obstacle. These robots are described as autonomous because they performed these acts without direct human intervention. In other words, the robots could sense their environment and make decisions on which actions to take in response to what they were sensing.

There is a delightful implicit contradiction in the term 'autonomous robot'. You may recall that the term 'robot' originates from the English translation of Karel Capek's 1920 play "Rossum's Universal Robots". Capek used the Czech word "robotnik" to describe the fictitious humanoid machines that featured in his play. Robotnik means "slave" and comes from the Old Church Slavonic word for *servitude*. So according to this the phrase 'autonomous robot' can be expanded to mean something like "the freely acting, self-governing, slave". The implicit contradiction in this phrase nicely characterises the much debated territory that we are just about to enter, namely the concept of free will itself.

There are those who would argue that free will is an illusion and that the phrase 'autonomous human' carries just as much of an implicit contradiction as does 'autonomous robot'. According to this view, whilst we appear to be self-governing and capable of acting freely, we are actually slaves to causal determinism in much the same way as robots are. This debate hits at the very heart of what we have come to understand about what it means to be human and what it means to be moral beings.

7.2. Free Will

In order to proceed with this discussion, we need to delve deeper into what we mean by acting freely. As we saw in the previous chapter, the source of freedom and the capacity for original action and creativity in the human self is the *will*. Willard organised the dimensions of the self into concentric circles, with the outer circle representing the *soul*, which in some sense contains the other dimensions through its integrative function. Moving inwards, the next circle represents the social context from which flows information and experience, that passes through the body into the mind and is presented to the will through thought and feeling.

Willard places the *will* at the centre not only because its function depends on this inward flow of information and experience, and the outward flow of action, but also because it steers the content of what is coming in and what is going out. The will is ultimately responsible for the condition of all of the dimensions of the self through which experience and action flow.

This steering operates at different times scales and in different ways, and is mediated by three primary functions of the will: (a) to give rise to original thought or new ideas, (b) to choose what the mind focusses on, and (c) to initiate the execution of what currently holds the attention of the mind. It is important, at this point, to be clear about what we mean by *original thought* or *new ideas*. These terms are not describing thoughts that nobody else, including ourselves, have ever thought before – although these are not ruled out. No, in this context we are using the terms to describe thoughts that did not arise from the *automatic thought habits* that we have developed. They are thoughts that have not automatically emerged from what is currently the focus of attention in the mind.

Let's illustrate this with a variant of our groceries example, this time from a human perspective. Imagine that our human shopper, let's call him David, normally goes to the nearby corner shop to get his groceries, and that this is the thought that habitually comes to mind whenever he thinks about going shopping. On one particular day, however, he has an inclination to go to the superstore instead and see what other brands and offers they have. David's will, in this case, would bring this new thought to the attention of the mind. So, the mind now has a choice placed before it. Go to the corner shop as usual, a choice which would automatically come to mind for him, or explore what the superstore has to offer. What David actually does will depend on a number of factors that come into play. But if his will is strongly set in favour of going to the superstore, and it is not overruled by the power of the habitual thought, then David will set out to go to the superstore.

It is important to note that whether David went to the corner shop or the superstore, in other words, whether he followed what his habitual thinking led him to do or whether what his will led him to do, both are ultimately outcomes of the operation of his free will. To understand this we must return to how the inner dimensions of the human self develop over time.

David's habit of going to the corner shop for his groceries had a beginning and that beginning was through the operation of his will. Suppose we turn back the clock to when David moved into the house he is now living in. Having just moved in David needed to buy groceries. He noticed that there was a corner shop nearby and he decided (act of the will) to go and investigate. He likes the shop and the shop keeper. After a few more visits David decides that he should shop there regularly. And so whenever he needs more groceries, he habitually thinks of going to the corner shop. The key point is that this habit was formed through the engagement of

David's will at various points in his past.

In this way, habitual thoughts, as well as 'new' thoughts, are primarily a product of human free will, that operates in the context of other influencing and constraining factors. This leads us on to a key point about *free will*, which is that the human will is never totally free. It is always constrained by (a) the way information flows to it from its social context, and (b) the capacity of the mind and the body.

What is presented to the mind, and hence to the will, about the individual's body and environment is always filtered. It is first of all filtered by the capacity of the senses to detect what is going on in the environment. Our senses and nervous system are tuned to detect certain signals from our environment (sights, smells, touch, temperature, taste etc.). But these are limited by what they can represent. So, for example, our eyesight is limited to a sub-range of the available radiation signals that flood our environment. Similarly our hearing is limited to a sub-range of sound pitches.

Furthermore, it is well known that our senses can be fooled. There is a classic study in psychology that illustrates this called 'the rubber hand experiment' in which a human participant is sat at a table with one of their hands underneath the table and hidden from view. On the table in front of them is a life-sized rubber hand. The experimenter uses feathers to simultaneously stroke both the rubber hand and the participant's hand that is under the table. The participant can see the rubber hand being stroked, and can feel their own hand being stroked at the same time. After being exposed to this for a period of time, the experimenter will stop stroking the hand that is under the table, but will continue to stroke the rubber hand. The participant will report that they can feel their hand is still being stroked, even though it is only the rubber hand that is being stroked. Their mind has been fooled into detecting this stroking sensation because that sensation has been associated with the visual cue of the rubber hand being stroked.

Surprisingly, though, our sensory perceptions are rarely fooled in this way. We have remarkably stable and accurate information presented to our minds from our senses. But that is not the end of the story, because what we sense, and how we interpret it depends on how those sensory signals are filtered and processed together.

Some people, for example, are attuned to detecting certain things that others would simply not observe, even though they are witnessing the same event, and receiving the same light, sound and touch signals. The neural circuits in our brain adapt over time to filter out the key bits of information that is most interesting and relevant to us as individuals.

A keen bird watcher, for example, will instantly recognise the musical phrases of a particular kind of songbird, which to many others would fall into the category of background noise. An expert wine taster will pick up senses from their taste buds and recognise a good quality wine, which many of us would not be able to distinguish from low cost products.

So the brain of every adult has become attuned to highlight some sensory signals and not others. This has an impact on what we perceive and as a consequence how we react to what we perceive, which in turn sets the extent of the freedom within which we can act. We cannot choose to act in response to something if we are unable to perceive it.

But our will is not just limited by what we can perceive, it is also limited by what is physically possible in the moment the will wishes to act. My youngest son, Joel, has always had big ambitions, even from an early age. When he was about 5 years old he came to me and asked "Dad, can we build a rocket out of cardboard in the garden? Then I could get into it and you could set fire to the bottom of it so that I could fly to the moon!" How do you begin to explain to a 5 year old that, not only will this cause him significant harm, but that it also wouldn't work. That really is rocket science! What he wanted to do was far beyond what he and his dad could do with a cardboard box and some matches in the garden.

Joel continued to conceive of many other ambitious and impossible schemes, and he was so utterly convinced that they could be done that we had a hard time explaining to him the limitations of what could be achieved in reality. He is older now, and, sadly, has grown out of that phase. I do miss it. But he now has a better understanding of the limitations of what can be realistically achieved. Through experience, his will has adapted and refocussed his ambitions in other directions.

Free Will and Determinism

So what we call 'free will' is rarely totally free. It is often constrained by both how we perceive the world, and what is physically possible in the moment of acting. But there has been much debate as to whether or not we posses even this limited notion of free will. The debate centres on the combination of two perspectives: (1) the mind-brain identity theory that asserts that the mind is identical to the brain, or rather to the states and processes that are within the brain (we shall return to this theory later in this section), and (2) the brain, like almost everything else in the universe, is subject to *causal determinism*. In this section we will briefly review the free-will and determinism debate, but note that this is a complex topic and it will be necessary to miss out significant amounts of detail on the different perspectives philosophers take on this issue[1].

Classical Newtonian physics asserts that all events that take place in the universe, including the ones inside our brains, are the result of a series of cause and effect chains: every event has a prior physical cause, without exception, even if those physical events are the thought processes in your mind. This is referred to as *universal physical determinism*, which was widely held to be true by philosophers and scientists up to the end of the nineteenth century.

---

[1]For example, some philosophers, like Robert Kane, hold to both libertarian free will and to the mind-brain identity theory, provided causal indeterminism holds. It seems, though, that most libertarian philosophers are dualists of some kind about the mind, rejecting the mind-brain identity theory. The question of whether libertarian free will entails the falsity of mind-brain identity is still very much a contested issue.

So why is universal physical determinism a problem for free will? The problem is that on the face of it they seem to be incompatible with each other. If our brains are subject to physical determinism, then the next thought we have is caused purely by the current physical *state* of our brains. Recall that brains are highly complex dynamical systems made up of many billions of microscopic components that emit and transfer electro-chemical impulses across densely interconnected networks. Living brains are always active and changing.

When we talk about the *state* of a brain, we are referring to a snapshot of electro-chemical activity of the brain, together with the location and arrangement of all the molecules (ions, proteins etc.) that facilitate the brain's operation. The deterministic nature of the physical processes in our brains is such that, any given particular brain state will result in a particular next brain state, which doesn't seem to leave any room for free choice.

Let's illustrate this issue by returning to our groceries shopper David. Imagine that we have two godly powers: the ability to examine David's brain state, and the ability to rewind time. Suppose that just prior to the moment of choice about where he will go shopping, we take note of David's brain state. Then in the next moment after David has decided to go to the superstore, we observe David's brain state again. If we use our godly power to rewind time back to the moment just prior to David's choice so that his brain is back in its original state, then causal determinism will require that his brain will go to exactly the same next state, which corresponds to choosing to shop at the superstore.

In a moment of godly playfulness, we decide to rewind time even further, back to when David was having his breakfast that morning. We take note of his brain state and observe that he wasn't even thinking about going shopping at that point. As we allow time to role forward again, causal determinism dictates that we will see exactly the same sequence of brain states emerging, corresponding to David making exactly the same 'choices' over the course of the morning, right up to where he decides to go to the superstore.

In other words, the outcome of his deliberation over where to go shopping was already causally determined by his brain state at breakfast. This causal chain of brain states goes right back to David's childhood; Every seemingly freely chosen thought and action throughout his life was caused by his very earliest brain states. If the outcomes of all our choices are already determined before we make them, then what room does that leave for 'free will'? On the face of it, free will does seems to be incompatible with causal determinism.

Some philosophers like Hume and Hobbes, however, have argued to the contrary, insisting that free will is indeed compatible with causal determinism. The core of this compatibilist argument centres on understanding freedom as the absence of constraints. According to this view, to be free you need to (a) have the ability to *do* what you want, and (b) not be blocked by doing what you want by any constraints. Since neither of these conditions contradicts causal determinism, you can still be endowed with the ability to *do* what you want as long as there are no constraints blocking that freedom.

This view that freedom is the absence of constraints is an interesting one that has a natural intuition. But the kind of freedom we are talking about is freedom of the will, which runs at a much deeper level than merely the absence of constraints to doing what we want. As we saw previously, the will is the source of freedom and the freedom is in the *wanting* rather than the acting. Compatibilists argue, though, that this freedom of the will can be treated in a similar way to freedom of action. Their two conditions can be re-framed to describe freedom of choice as follows: we have freedom of choice if (a) we have the ability to *choose* something, (b) there are no constraints on us making that choice.

The next step in the compatibilist's argument makes the link between causal determinism and free will as the absence of constraints. To illustrate this, let's enact our godly powers on David and his shopping dilemma once again. Imagine that David really gives this some thought, and weighs up all the pros and cons of each option: the corner shop is closer, its good to support local businesses, on the other hand the superstore has more choice and often lower prices. Then David arrives at a decision, he will go to the superstore.

If we then rewind time to the point when David first began to think about going shopping, causal determinism would dictate that, starting at the same brain state, he would go through exactly the same rational thought processes and end up making the same decision as the first time. If, they argue, the outcome of the rerun of his thought processes was that David decided to go to the local shop instead, then that would constitute a *non-deterministic* outcome, which according to them would be irrational. Determinism means if you repeat the same past, you get the same future. Non-determinism means if you repeat the same past, you do not necessarily get the same future.

The argument is quite compelling. The sense of free will that many of us hold to is that we have ultimate control over the direction of our will, which is not determined completely by our past. But compatabilists argue that if we do operate in this way with non-deterministic outcomes to our decision making, then this is incoherent and infeasible. It amounts to going through life making random choices – which is, in effect, making no choices at all.

It should be noted, though, that all of this is founded on the assumption that the will, and more generally the mind, is subject to physical or causal determinism. An interesting twist in the story of causal determinism and free will came with the advent of quantum physics, which radically challenged the classic scientific view that the entire universe was subject to causal determinism, a view that was called *universal physical determinism*. The discovery which led to this remarkable u-turn was made in particle physics.

In brief, the issue is centred on the fact that sub-atomic elements exhibit properties of both particles and waves, and the state and position of these elements could not be known with certainty. The prevailing theory in quantum physics is centred on Heisenberg's uncertainty principle which is that particles do not have an exact position and momenta at the same time. Consequently, it is not physically possible to predict their future behaviour. It is argued, therefore, that physical determinism does not exist at the sub-atomic particle level and the majority of physical scientists no longer believe in universal physical determinism.

The fact that *universal* physical determinism is no longer a viable scientific proposition does not remove the issue of its compatibility with free will. Although events at the sub-atomic level are not causally determined, it is clear that on larger scales causal determinism is still at play. When a force is applied to a physical object, the direction and speed with which it moves can still be predicted accurately using formulas based on causal determinism. It is reasonable to ask, though, whether quantum indeterminism has an influence on the processes that occur in the brain. Does it occur on a large enough scale for the sub-atomic uncertainty to have an affect on neuronal firing patterns, for example? The current scientific consensus is that quantum effects are too small to have an impact on the brain, and that the brain is still subject to causal determinism.

The presumption that the mind is identical to the physical processes in the brain is a perspective that is proposed by the *mind-brain identity theory.* If the mind-brain identity holds, then, as many philosophers and scientists have concluded, causal determinism means that our experience of free will is an illusion. There would be no freedom to choose, because the will itself would be the product of the underlying physical processes in the brain. These processes alone would determine our wants and our choices.

As we explored in the previous chapter, however, general Christian thought is that the will is *spirit* not flesh. If this is the case, then it takes the will out of the realm of the physical determinism that the body is subject to. In fact, Willard would argue that the whole mind – will, thought and feeling – is non-physical, but is of course deeply connected with the body, and in particular with the brain. He was a *dualist* after all, maintaining that the mind and the brain are radically different kinds of things. There is much that can be said here about the mind-body problem, but it would distract us too much from our current mission, which is to understand the relationship between the nature of the will and physical determinism.

If the will is indeed essentially a non-physical entity that is connected to the body, then surely that side-steps the issue of it being subjected to physical determinism. The compatibilist's response to this suggestion is simply to shift the same argument to the non-physical level. It goes something like this. If David's choice of where to go shopping is ultimately made in the non-physical realm, then imagine the same 'ground hog day' loop, where he goes through exactly the same thought process (this time non-physical) and reaches a decision. If this process is non-deterministic (i.e. he doesn't *necessarily* make the same decision he did the first time around the loop) then that too is still incoherent and irrational.

The problem with this last move by the compatibilists is that it is attempting to apply physical determinism to an entity that is not physical. In other words it seeks to bring the spiritual realm within the constraints of the physical realm. One thing that is abundantly clear when we read the Bible is that entities in the spiritual realm were often not constrained by physical laws. Angels appear in the air, defying the law of gravity. Even physical entities could violate physical laws when associated with spiritual beings.

Take, for example, the account in the gospels after Jesus' *bodily* resurrection. He miraculously entered a locked room and stood among his terrified disciples who thought he was a ghost. But he reassured them that he was truly, physically present by saying "Why are you troubled, and why do doubts rise in your minds? Look at my hands and my feet. It is I myself! Touch me and see; a ghost does not have flesh and bones, as you see I have"[2]. And then, to prove that he was there in flesh and bones, he ate some broiled fish as they watched. By entering a locked room in that way, Jesus' body violated the laws of physics and the causal determinism that they insist on.

There are many other accounts in the Bible of the laws of physics being broken when the spiritual meets the physical. So we cannot simply presume that the spiritual nature of the will is constrained

[2]Luke 24:38 NIV

by physical determinism. Neither can we presume that the concept of 'state', on which physical determinism rests, can be used to describe the condition of the spirit or will of a person. That is applying materialistic thinking to the non-material.

The assertion that the will is not material, and that it is not constrained to make the same decisions on the ground hog day loop, does not mean that its decisions are *necessarily* irrational. What it does mean is that it has a *capacity* that operates beyond the constraints of causal determinism to reach a decision. Perhaps this capacity is facilitated through additional 'heavenly' dimensions that give the person's spirit a perspective this is beyond what is achievable in the physical universe.

An example from the world of machine learning may help to illustrate this possibility. There is a class of machine learning algorithm called a *linear classifiers* that make decisions based on simple ('linear') separations of the input data, as illustrated in Figure 7.1(a). This figure shows data that is plotted according to two features that might represent, for example, the height versus weight of two groups (e.g. adults and children). The data items from one class is represented using a '+', whilst the data items from the other class are represented with an 'o'. In Figure 7.1(a), the two groups or 'clusters' are easily separated by a linear classifier, as illustrated by the straight line. New data points can be classified into one cluster or the other (e.g. adult or child) depending on which side of the line they come.

The clusters in Figure 7.1(b), on the other hand, are impossible for a linear classifier to separate. Note that the class represented by '+' is split in two clusters; one in the bottom right and the other in the top left of the plot. Similarly the class represented by 'o' is split into two clusters at the top right and bottom left of the figure. It is not possible to draw a single straight line that separates the top left and bottom right clusters from the top right and bottom left clusters. Try it and see.

One way to get around this problem is to use what is described in

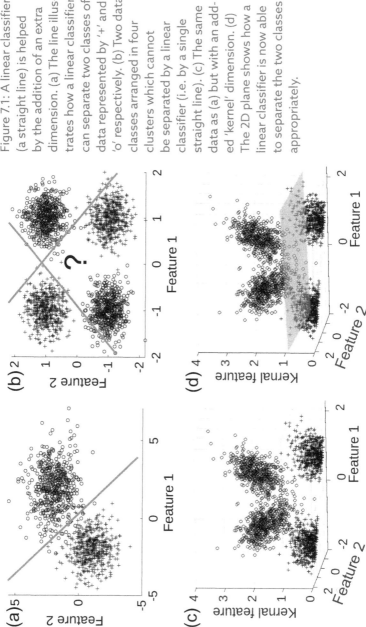

Figure 7.1: A linear classifier (a straight line) is helped by the addition of an extra dimension. (a) The line illustrates how a linear classifier can separate two classes of data represented by '+' and 'o' respectively. (b) Two data classes arranged in four clusters which cannot be separated by a linear classifier (i.e. by a single straight line). (c) The same data as (a) but with an added 'kernel' dimension. (d) The 2D plane shows how a linear classifier is now able to separate the two classes appropriately.

machine learning as a 'kernel trick' which involves using a function (the 'kernel') that projects the data into a higher dimensional space. In this case we can take advantage of the fact that the features of the bottom left and top right clusters have the same sign (e.g. [-1,-1] or [1,1] for 'o'), whereas features in the top left and bottom right have opposite signs (e.g. [-1,1] or [1,-1] for '+'). A simple 'kernel' function can use the absolute value of the sum of the features (*abs(Feature1 + Feature2)*) to project the data into a third dimension, as shown in Figure 7.1(c). As you can see, the data points for 'o' are pushed higher up in the 'kernel feature', making them easily separable by a linear classifier (Figure 7.1(d))[3]

Just as the addition of an extra dimension using the 'kernel function' overcame the limitations of the linear classifier in our example, so the availability of a 'heavenly' dimension in the form of a person's spirit has the *potential* to overcome the limitations of causal determinism in the brain.

Spirit and Brain Interaction

But this proposition opens up another problem for us. If the source of free will in a person is their spirit, how does this heavenly, non-material entity interact with a material brain. This interaction must occur if the spirit is to have any influence over the body at all. Furthermore, this interaction must be two-way: the spirit influences the brain, but the brain must also influence the spirit. In fact, it seems as though the two are mutually bound to each other during the life of the individual.

We know from brain injury studies and from the effect of degenerative brain diseases that reduced brain function has an impact on an individual's awareness and capacity for thought[4]. Theological-

[3]Note that the line that represented the linear classifier in the 2D case become a plane in the 3D case.

[4]Eamonn Walsh, David A. Oakley, Peter W. Halligan, Mitul A. Mehta, Quinton Deeley, Brain mechanisms for loss of awareness of thought and movement, Social Cognitive and Affective Neuroscience, Volume 12, Issue 5, May 2017, Pages 793–801, https://doi.org/10.1093/scan/nsw185

ly, awareness and thought are core capacities of spiritual entities, including of course God himself.

How is this mutual interaction and dependency between a non-material spirit and a material body possible? Does the spirit take control of a particular part of the brain such as the lateral prefrontal cortex, as proposed in the VirtuosA model presented in Chapter 6? Perhaps. There is the sense, though, that although the two are bound to each other, they also possess a degree of independence.

In our discussion of Willard's model of the human self, we identified situations in which the other dimensions of the self were at odds with the heart/will/spirit dimension. There are echo's of this in Paul's letter to the Romans in which he says "I do not understand what I do. For what I want to do I do not do, but what I hate I do."[5] According to Willard's perspective, Paul's will is in conflict with the rest of his personality that is embodied by his soul, and which the soul 'farms out' to his body, primarily his brain.

To frame our thinking about this, the first step is to take note of the nature of reality as it is presented in the Bible. Right at the outset, creation is presented as a dual reality: "In the beginning God created the *heavens* and the *earth*."[6] The phrase "the heavens and the earth" refers to all created things. The "heavens" describes not just the sky, but also the spiritual reality in which the heavenly beings live and the place from which God speaks and acts.

The deep connection between the heavens and the earth is repeatedly emphasised in scripture, especially in references to renewal and the prophesies about a "new heaven and new earth."[7] Humans reflect this dual reality that they inhabit by being dual in nature; an integration of both heaven (spirit) and earth (body).

But the question remains, how does this dual reality operate in practice? How do the spirit and the brain interact whilst maintaining a balance between mutual dependence and individual independence? One possible, tentative answer to these questions comes in the form of chaos theory.

---

[5]Romans 7:15
[6]Genesis 1:1
[7]Isaiah 65:17, 66:22, Acts 14:15, Revelation 21:1

Back in the 1990's, chaos was all the rage. I'm not talking about riots or fashion or music, I'm talking about mathematics. Several popular science books were published on the subject, including *Chaos: Making a New Science* by James Gleick and *Does God Play Dice?: The New Mathematics of Chaos* by Ian Stewart. Chaos theory even made an appearance in the original Jurrasic Park feature film. One of the main characters in the movie was Dr Ian Malcom, played by Jeff Goldblum, who was a mathematician with expertise in chaos theory. In one particular scene, Dr Malcom explains chaos using an illustration of water droplets moving down the hand of palaeontologist Ellie Sattler. What he was attempting to do, apart from sweet talk Sattler, was to illustrate a fundamental defining property of chaotic systems called 'sensitivity to initial conditions'. To get our heads around this and why it feeds into our current discussion about a potential spirit-brain interface, we need to to a bit of ground work.

Chaotic dynamics are a feature of many physical and abstract systems. Classically, the weather is widely regarded as being governed by chaotic dynamics. But the weather is too complex to use as an illustration here. Let's stick with Malcom's much simpler illustration of water by imaging that we have a dripping tap. Starting from the off position, if you turn the tap on slightly, enough to allow a small amount of water through, drips will start to form on the tap outlet, and will eventually drop into the sink. To begin with, these might be evenly timed drips: "drip...drip...drip". This forms a nice, regular drip pattern which mathematician's call a a *period one oscillation*.

If you turn the tap on just a little bit more, what you then find is the pattern changes, often to a "drip-drip...drip-drip" pattern: two drips in quick succession, followed by a pause, then another two drips. In mathematical terms, the period of this sequence has doubled.

If it were possible to have fine-grained control over the amount of water flowing out of the tap, you would find that as you turn the tap on a little bit more, the period doubles again to four, and then 16. After just a few more turns of the tap something remarkable happens, the period of the dripping goes to infinity. In other words, the pattern of time gaps between drips never repeats. The dripping water has moved into chaotic dynamics – a never repeating pattern of activity. What you have observed in this tap experiment is what is called *the period doubling route to chaos*.

Many other systems exhibit these chaotic dynamics, including irregular heart rhythms, ocean turbulence and the stock market. What unifies them all are the characteristics of chaos, the most significant of which for our purposes is *sensitivity to initial conditions*. This characteristic is often used to measure the presence and extent of chaos in the dynamics of a system. The property of sensitivity to initial conditions is, as its name suggests, where the evolving state of the system can be radically changed by even the smallest change in its initial state.

To illustrate, let us return to the weather. Back in the 1960's, meteorologist Edward Lorenz developed a set of mathematical equations for modelling the phenomena of atmospheric convection – the cyclic movement of volumes of air in the atmosphere. In particular, he developed a set of equations for studying the circulation of fluid in a shallow layer that was heated from the bottom and cooled from above. The fluid was assumed to circulate in both horizontal and vertical directions and be contained within a rectangular boundary. Lorenz used three variables to model the state of the fluid: x was related to the rate of convection, y to the variation in horizontal temperature, and z to the variation in vertical temperature.

One of the ways dynamical systems like this are studied is to plot the values of the variables against each other as they evolve in time using what is called a *phase plot*. If you create such a plot for a chaotic system like the Lorenz equations, you find that the values of the state variables will converge onto a surface within the phase plot which is called an *attractor* (Figure 7.2)[8]. As we shall see, this property of sensitivity to initial conditions leads to two somewhat surprising features of chaotic systems that are pertinent to our discussion on spirit-brain interaction.

---

[8]The Lorenz system exists in three dimensions corresponding to the values of its x, y and z variables. The phase plot in Figure 7.2 shows only the x and z dimensions.

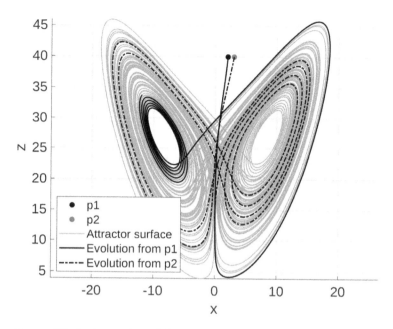

Figure 7.2: A phase plot of the Lorenz attractor demonstrating the sensitivity to initial conditions property of chaos, plotted in the x and z dimensions. The time evolution of the system from two nearby starting points p1 and p2 are shown, illustrating that a small change in initial conditions (from p1 to p2) ultimately results in radically different evolutions of the system.

There is a good deal of evidence of the presence of chaotic dynamics in the brain. Neuroscientists have measured the activity of neurons in animals in response to various stimuli (e.g. smells, tastes etc.) and observed that this activity has properties that align with those of chaotic systems. It is important to note, though, that there is no conclusive evidence that the activity in the brain is chaotic; the complexity of the brain makes it difficult to draw such conclusions. Also, it is difficult to be sure that the activity you are observing in the brain is driven by chaos rather than randomness. In many respects these two look similar[9].

Nevertheless, some neuroscientists are convinced that chaotic dynamics underlie the signalling patterns of the neurons on the mammalian brain. Much work has been done in recent years to discover the advantages that chaotic dynamics might bring to the information processing capabilities of the brain. I have contributed to some of this work through studies that I conducted in the field of computational neuroscience. *Computational neuroscience* involves the creation of biologically plausible computer models of the brain, and in particular of neurons, and studying their behaviour under different conditions.

I created one such model which I call the *Nonlinear Dynamic State* (NDS) neuron. The NDS neuron model has a dynamic internal state that is modelled by three time-dependent variables: $u(t)$, which represents the degree of electrical activation of the neuron, and $x(t)$ and $y(t)$ that represent other time dependent internal conditions of the neuron. The time-varying values of these three variables are driven by a chaotic attractor.

Whenever the activation ($u(t)$) reaches a particular threshold value ('0'), the neuron fires, sending an action potential to the other neurons to which it is connected. This firing behaviour is illustrated in Figure 7.3(a), which show a short sample of the time series of the activation (lower part of the plot, below 0) and firing (upper part of the plot, above 0)of the neuron. The arrows show the time evolution of the activation. You will see that in this sample the neuron fires twice. Figure 7.3(b) shows the corresponding phase plot, with the neuron's activation $u(t)$ plotted against internal state variable *$x(t)$.*

One of the primary advantages that chaos offers the brain is the potential for a *rich set of dynamics* to support its information processing requirements. What I mean by 'rich set of dynamics' is that chaos

---

[9]Chaos and randomness are quite different from each other. Chaos is deterministic, randomness is not. Also, unlike randomness, a chaotic system is sensitive to initial conditions. But because chaos is, by definition, a non-repeating pattern of activity, it can appear to be random to the observer.

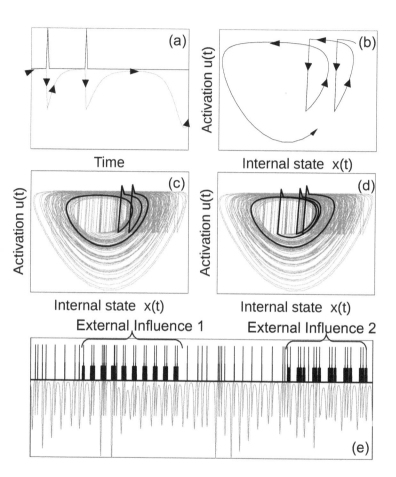

Figure 7.3: Data from the Nonlinear Dynamical State neuron that is subject to external influence.

makes available a wide range of dynamical features for the brain to draw upon as it represents and processes information. Let's take a look at one such feature: the Unstable Periodic Orbit (UPO).

One of the surprising features of many chaotic systems is the ease with which they can be controlled. Due to its sensitivity to initial conditions, small instantaneous changes ('nudges') to the state of a chaotic system can cause it to repeat a dynamic path within phase space. Remember that by definition chaos is a non-repeating pattern of activity. But small, repeated and well timed 'nudges' can push the trajectory of the dynamical system in phase space back to where it had previously been so that the systems repeats the trajectory it had just completed. These repeated trajectories are called Unstable Periodic Orbits; they are unstable because, without the appropriately timed nudges, the system would move away from the periodic orbit towards a different area of the attractor.

This control of chaos is one of the features of the NDS neuron model. Figure 7.3(e) shows the time series of an extended run of the model. During the first 1000 time steps of the run, the model is free to follow its internal chaotic dynamics. You will note that the activation $(u(t))$ and the firing patterns of the neuron during this phase are irregular. Then between time steps 1000 and 2000, an external influence (EI1) is applied to the model in the form of a repeated pattern of two 'nudges'. It is important to note that in between these nudges, the model is free to follow its chaotic dynamics. Note that part way through this first external influence stage, the model falls into a repeated pattern or UPO in which it fires twice. Plot (c) in Figure 7.3 shows this UPO superimposed onto the NDS neuron attractor.

Following the removal of external influence 1, the neuron returns to its chaotic activity until a second external influence is introduced at time step 3000, this time subjecting the model to a repeated pattern of three nudges. Once again, this nudging leads the neuron to fall into another UPO, which is shown in Figure 7.3(d).

We ran experiments on the NDS neuron model and discovered that it could fall into over 6,000 *different* UPOs, each with its own unique spiking pattern of action potentials. In other words, the neuron could be in any one of these dynamic states, and it could communicate to other neighbouring neurons which dynamic state it was in though the associated unique spike train. This is like giving the neuron a vocabulary of upwards of 6,000 words with it could 'talk' to other neurons.

Although, through experimental runs, we discovered over 6,000 UPOs, it is likely that the model has significantly more, as yet undiscovered UPOs. In fact, a feature of chaotic attractors in general is that they embed a theoretically infinite number of UPOs. These are the rich dynamics that I introduced earlier. Imagine for a moment that the mammalian brain is chaotic, and imagine also that each UPO in the brain's chaotic attractor corresponds to a thought (this is a gross over-simplification, but let's run with the idea for now). This would mean that the brain has a limitless capacity in terms of the number of different thoughts it could potentially entertain, which is an awesome possibility!

Now, with that context in mind, we have something to say about the spirit-brain interface. Bear in mind that what I am about to describe is speculation-informed speculation at best. Imagine that, instead of taking total control of the brain or a sub-region of it, the spirit had the capacity to 'nudge' certain areas of the brain such as the lateral prefrontal cortex. And imagine that those nudges corresponded to a particular thought held by the spirit. If the spirit-brain interface operates as I've suggested, and if the nudges are appropriately timed, then the brain will be nudged into a dynamic state (UPO) that corresponds to that thought.

If this is indeed how the spirit-brain interface works, then we can see a way for the spirit to fulfil two of its primary functions:

(a) to give rise to original thought or new ideas, and (b) to choose what the mind focusses on. Being unconstrained by the limits of the material universe, the spirit has limitless capacity to create new thoughts, and the 'chaotic' brain has limitless capacity to entertain them. And since the spirit is not constrained by physical causation, these thoughts are not determined by the previous state of the brain.

It is worth noting at this point that by definition an unconstrained chaotic system like the brain will automatically go on to new, previously unvisited orbits on its attractor. But these new 'thoughts' are always determined by the previous instantaneous states of the brain. Chaos is, by definition, deterministic. The first primary function of the spirit is to enable a non-deterministic freedom of choice that steers the deterministic behaviour of the brain towards the thoughts that encapsulate the free choices made by the will.

The second primary function of the spirit is to hold the attention of the mind on particular thoughts. In terms of a brain that is governed by chaotic dynamics, this means repeatedly 'nudging' the brain so that it remains within the UPO that corresponds to that thought for as long as the will wants to focus on it. As we saw previously, this capacity of the will to hold the attention of the mind on specific thoughts is crucial to the moral development of a person.

The key thing about this way of thinking of the spirit-brain interface is that the spirit only nudges the brain, it doesn't take complete control of it, not even for a short period, as would have to be the case if the dynamics of the brain were not chaotic. This means that the brain, and in particular the learned patterns of thought and behaviour that it embodies, can still hold sway in the individual who may still find themselves in the predicament that Paul expresses: "I do not understand what I do. For what I *want* to do I do not do, but what I hate, I do."

Free Will and Predestination

We are not out of the woods yet with the concept of human autonomy and free will. Physical causation is not the only kind of determinism we need to contend with. There is also *theistic determinism*, which is associated with the theological concept of *predestination*: the capacity of God to pre-determine and arrange for the final 'destination' of the universe and its inhabitants. We do not have the space here to deal with this issue in depth, but I do want to briefly address two particular aspects that commonly lead to misunderstandings about free will in this area: pre-knowledge and predestination.[10]

Many people struggle with the notion that God knows the paths that our lives will take before we take them, or even before we are born, as described in verses like this from Psalm 139:

> "Your eyes saw my unformed body; all the days ordained for me were written in your book before one of them came to be". Psalm 139:16 NIV

The problem that people have with this is that they associate *pre-knowledge* with causation. If God knows ahead of time what I'm going to do, then surely I am constrained (by him) to take that path and my freedom to choose what path I take is nullified.

But this tendency to equate divine fore-knowledge with causation is erroneous. It is quite easy to show that fore-knowledge does not entail causation. Imagine for a moment that you see me holding a vase at arms length above the floor. I tell you that I am going to let go of that vase and I ask you to predict where it will end up after I let go. You say that it will be smashed to pieces on the floor in front of me. I let go of the vase, and low and behold, you are correct in your prediction, it does end up smashed to pieces on the floor in front of me. I then claim that because you had *fore-knowledge* of where the vase would end up, that you *caused* it to arrive there and be smashed to pieces. You would legitimately content that that is a ridiculous accusation. Fore-knowledge simply does not imply causation. It simply means that you have knowledge ahead of time how things are going to end up. Similarly, God's foreknowledge of the paths we will *choose* to take in our lives and the spiritual condition we will end up in, does not mean that he caused us to make those choices.

But the New Testament makes other claims about predestination that seem to many to eliminate human autonomy and free will

---

[10]For a thorough and accessible discussion on this subject I refer to you John Lennox's book 'Determined to Believe?: The Sovereignty of God, Freedom, Faith and Human Responsibility' published by Monarch Books

altogether. In his letters to the Romans and Ephesians, Paul makes multiple references to them being predestined by God, and in verse 29 of Romans 8 he links fore-knowledge with predestination:

> "For those God foreknew he also predestined to be conformed to the image of his Son, that he might be the firstborn among many brothers and sisters." Romans 8:29 NIV.

But, like fore-knowledge, pre-destination doesn't necessarily entail causation and the elimination of free will. Let's return to our vase example to illustrate. Imagine that after I announce that I'm going to let go of the vase, you quickly grab a cushion and put it on the floor where you know it is going to land, and indeed when I do let go, the vase lands safely on the cushion without breaking. You have used your fore-knowledge to pre-arrange for a different *destination* (the cushion as opposed to the floor), and consequently a different outcome (the vase does not smash to pieces). Your capacity to arrange this pre-destined landing site played no part in the physical causality (i.e. gravity) that resulted from me letting go of it, until it reached that destination (the cushion). God's predestination of those he foreknew does not overrule their free will, but anticipates where their freely made choices will take them so that he can prepare their ultimate destination and condition ("conformed to the image of his Son").

7.3. Ultimate Responsibility

The question we are seeking to address in this chapter is to what extent, if at all, robot autonomy is the same as human autonomy. What kind of freedom can a robot have, if any? Even if we are able to simulate with a high degree of accuracy Willard's five dimensions of the self, including the operation of the will, does that constitute a kind of autonomy that resembles what humans experience? The answers to these questions will then inform our thinking about whether or not robots should be held responsible for the actions that they autonomously perform, as illustrated in the 'Trial of Alex Montague' short story.

We need to turn our attention to considering what freedom would actually mean to a robot and whether or not all robots posses it, or only some. And if only some of them possess it, what characteristics of these select few are definitive with respect to freedom and true autonomy. Let's start with K9d who was the cause of an industrial accident (or murder and theft?) in our short story from Part I. To what extent did K9d have autonomy? It certainly was not behaving as the night duty engineer expected, and was making movements that exceeded prescribed movement limits. If these movements were unanticipated, either by the night duty engineer or by the designers of the robot, does that constitute autonomous action? Here are two definitions of robot autonomy:

> "An autonomous robot . . . is a robot that performs behaviours or tasks with a high degree of autonomy (without external influence)." [11]

> "Autonomous robots are intelligent machines capable of performing tasks in the world by them-selves, without explicit human control." Autonomous Robots, G.A. Bekey, MIT Press

By these definitions, K9d was an autonomous robot. In its normal fully functional state, it could independently scan the conveyor belt and recognise different objects for recycling, decide which category of recycling each belonged to, then pick them up and put them in the correct recycling tray. The robot is deciding how to act according to what it sees on the conveyor belt – or is it?

Before we attempt to answer that, consider also K9d in its

---

[11]WikiPedia (accessed 17/02/2021)

apparent malfunctioning state. The engineer found that it had not returned to its arm-folded, shut-down position, as instructed. But instead had its arm stretched out away from the conveyor belt and towards the vending machine. It looked like the robot was reaching for the chocolate – but we all know that it wasn't. Also, consider its 'decision' to scan the engineer as it worked on the robot, detect his wallet, and then pick and place it in one of its valuable objects bin, and in the process killing the engineer. Are these autonomous actions too? Well, according to the above definitions, yes, absolutely. All of them were autonomous, even the ones that appear to be the result of a malfunction.

If K9d's actions were truly autonomous in the sense that we discussed in the previous section, then surely the robot would be held responsible for its actions. Yet this seems a step too far for most people. This suggests that what we mean by robot autonomy does not align with what we mean by human autonomy. Though the difference between these two versions of autonomy is not entirely clear.

Autonomy in humans is usually associated with the capacity to do what we want to do. Much of our behaviour emerges from our wants and desires. To what extent can a robot possess these wants and desires? Well, it is possible to simulate the wanting and desiring. In other words, you could create a robot which behaves as though it has wants and desires – but these are fake, and at best implied by people observing and interacting with the robot through their natural tendency to anthropomorphise them. "Look, the robot wants to help you learn maths". This surface level appearance of wanting is little more than a sophisticated puppet on strings that are pulled by the robots designer.

A more genuine approach might be to attempt to represent wanting and desiring somehow in the inner core of the robots being, as proposed in the VirtuosA architecture in Chapter 6. This has been done many times by many roboticists. But they would shy away from using terms like 'wanting' and 'desiring' because of the hard-to-define emotional content these words carry. Instead they would most likely use the term 'goal', because it captures the idea of something the robot can attempt to achieve, without having to complicate it with feelings and emotions.

So what is a goal in the context of robotics? Here's a useful definition: "Goals are abstractions of high-dimensional world states that express intelligent agents' intentions underlying their actions."[12] Let's unpack this definition. First of all, note the absence of words that have associated emotional content. This is very typical of researchers in AI. Second, we need to be clear about what is meant by the term 'abstraction'. An abstraction is a representation of an entity that maps onto it in some definable way. This is best illustrated with an example. Suppose the delivery robot we considered in the previous chapter had the task of delivering groceries to location D (Figure 6.1). How might this be represented as a goal? One way of doing this is to represent the state of the world that would be achieved if the goal is satisfied. We could use a list (technically, an 'array' or 'vector') to represent this goal state as shown in Table 7.1.

Robot location:	(1,8)
Robot holding	-
D contains	Groceries

Table 7.1: A representation of the goal to deliver groceries to location D

This describes the target state of the world just after the robot has delivered supplies to D. The robot's location is represented using 2 numbers which are the x and y position of the square that is next to the delivery point, and the robot is holding nothing, whilst square D contains the groceries. This list is an abstraction of this particular arrangement of the world that the robot inhabits, an arrangement that it will attempt to achieve using the various actions that it has at

[12]Rolf, M. and Asada, M., 2014. Where do goals come from? A generic approach to autonomous goal-system development. arXiv preprint arXiv:1410.5557

its disposal (e.g. pick up groceries, move north, etc.).

In this way, a robot can have a goal, which is like an intention, and it can have the means for achieving that goal. Those means involve the capacity to make 'decisions' on what needs to be done to achieve that goal, especially if there are multiple ways of satisfying the goal. These decisions, however, are essentially functions or formula that are coded into the robot ahead of time. The formula will typically calculate a numeric value for each option (e.g. a higher numeric value for more efficient paths). When a decision has to be made – the robot applies the formula and takes the option with the highest value. This seems to be quite different to what we mean when humans take decisions. Humans don't seem to have a pre-computed formula in their brains which essentially computes which decisions to take. Nevertheless, this is typically what is meant by robot autonomy – a robot that is capable of performing a task (e.g. navigation) by making a series of decisions on how to achieve that task without direct human intervention.

But does this mechanistic process really constitute autonomous action? If the robot is given the goal, and it is given the means for achieving that goal, including the functions it uses make apparent choices as and when needed, then where is the autonomy? In what sense is this robot acting on its own volition and capable of achieving what it wants?

Let's take it a step further. What if the robot wasn't given the goals at the outset; what if it was capable of creating its own novel goals[13]? Surely this would bring it closer to what we mean by human autonomy. But how is this possible? How could a robot create a novel goal? Well, if a goal is essentially a future state of the world, one way to do this would simply be to randomly create a future world state and set that as a goal. It is easy to see, though, that whilst the robot would be generating novel goals, their randomness would mean that they would not necessarily be rational, meaningful or achievable in the world in which the robot operates. Furthermore, randomly generated goals will simply result in random robot behaviour that will not

---

[13]Rolf, M. and Crook, N.T., 2016. What If: Robots Create Novel Goals? Ethics Based on Social Value Systems. In EDIA@ ECAI (pp. 20-25)

necessarily achieve the underlying task at hand (i.e. deliver groceries).

An alternative approach is to generate novel goals that are aligned with some overall purpose of the robot. If, for example, a robot was equipped with a value system of some kind that expressed a subjective goodness of a particular world state (i.e. potential goal). Then novel goals could be generated by identifying what future states would be good for the robot to achieve. Consider, for example, a robot that had the capability of recognising the needs of the people around them. Our groceries robot might, for example, be able to recognise that a person is struggling to carry their shopping home, and might be motivated, then, to generate a novel goal to approach them to offer to help them with their shopping, as we considered in the last chapter. This would require quite a sophisticated capability on the part of the robot, but it is not beyond the realms of possibility.

Even if we achieve this level of sophistication in novel goal creation in our robots, the goal creation process itself will always be subject to physical determinism. Novel goals, whether randomly generated (bearing in mind that computers are algorithmically driven and incapable of generating truly random sequences), or generated to align with the overall purpose of the robot, are always going to be pre-determined by the robot's state. At best, robots could at some point be credited with the compatibalist's version of free will, which as we have seen falls short of what we commonly think of as free will and autonomy in human beings

Ultimately it all depends, of course, on the nature of reality, on what free will actually is and how it is facilitated in humans. If you take a materialist perspective, you will have to contend with the question of whether free will is compatible with the causal determinism of the brain. You would need to re-think what free will and autonomy actually mean, if they mean anything at all.

If, on the other hand, humans are more than biological machines, if we are an integral part of this heaven-and-earth reality that the Bible repeatedly talks about, if we are both spirit and body, and if this spirit is not constrained by physical determinism in the way that our bodies are, then the kind of free will and autonomy that we all perceive and experience is not an illusion, it is reality. In this version of reality there is a wonderful balance between the predictability of causal determinism – which is absolutely necessary for us to be able to live and interact with the world (imagine a world in which all our actions had unpredictable consequences – how would we live with that?) – and the freedom to choose how to act, within the limits of what the will can conceive and what the body can perform.

If this is the reality we live in, then robots will never have the same degree of autonomy that humans have. No matter how cleverly we programme them, they will always be simulations of humans and of their capacity to exercise free will and autonomy. And as simulations of free will and autonomy, robots should never be held accountable for their own actions, because their actions are always going to be algorithmically determined and not freely chosen. Ultimate responsibility for a robot's action must rest with its human creators.

Chapter 8

THE MORAL SINGULARITY

"The development of full artificial intelligence
could spell the end of the human race."
Prof Stephen Hawking

Statements like these have been made by a number of prominent personalities and thought leaders in recent years, which has no doubt increased the level of anxiety that the general public have about AI powered machines. But what lies at the heart of this anxiety is not so much about robot autonomy, which we know is critical from a moral agency perspective, but intelligence, and more specifically *super-intelligence*. It is the fear that as machines become smarter and their capacity for thinking and analysis increases, there will be an inevitable moment when those machines will become more intelligent than humans. This event is commonly described as the *technological singularity*.

There are many who fear the social, economic and political impact of the technological singularity. Stephen Hawking, for example, warns that we should prepare ourselves for the possibility of our machine-based super-intelligence "...outsmarting financial markets, out-inventing researchers, out-manipulating human leaders, and developing weapons we cannot even understand".[1] In his book, "The People vs Tech: How the Internet is Killing Democracy

---

[1]Stephen Hawking (2014) "Transcendence looks at the implications of Artificial Intelligence. The Independent, 5th May 2014

(and How We Can Save It)", Jamie Bartlett predicts the destruction of six pillars of democracy that the unconstrained advancement of technology will bring about. But his most interesting prediction, from our perspective, is that of the 'moral singularity', a point in time when super-intelligent machines become far better at moral reasoning than humans, and as a consequence humans will delegate their moral and political reasoning to them. But how realistic are these predictions of the technical and moral singularity and where does that place humans in the created order?

8.1. What is a Singularity?

In its simplest terms, a singularity refers to a sudden explosive increase in the magnitude of one quantity (e.g. machine intelligence) as a result of a small incremental change in another dependent quantity (e.g. the underlying technology). In mathematics, this can be illustrated by the simple function:

$$f(x) = -\frac{1}{x}$$

If you plot this function against values of x starting from, say, $x = -12$ on a graph as illustrated in Figure 8.1, you will note an increase in $f(x)$ as you increase x. Let's look at some values of x and the corresponding values of $f(x)$. For relatively low values of x, we observe only small changes in $f(x)$, so that when $x = -10$, for example, $f(-10) = 0.1$, and if we increase x by 1 then we get $f(-9) = 0.111...$, an increase of 0.011 But for the same small change in the value of x closer to 0, we see a much bigger increase in $f(x)$. $f(-2)$, for example, gives 0.5, whereas $f(-1) = 1$, a change in $f(x)$ that is 45 times as big as the change from $f(-10)$ to $f(-9)$.

The rate at which $f(x)$ increases for small increases in x as it approaches 0 is described in mathematical terms an exponential

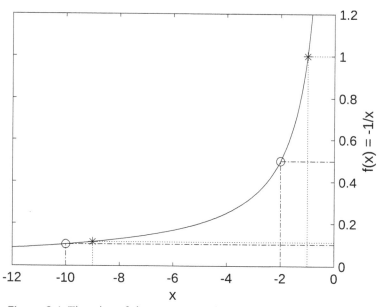

Figure 8.1: The plot of the exponential function f (x) = −1/x

function. But when x = 0, f (x) suddenly becomes infinitely large (mathematically, f (0) is not defined, since the division 1/0 cannot be calculated). This point, where x = 0, is a singularity – a point in which the small change in one value (e.g. from x = −0.0001, to x = 0), has a huge impact (f (0) = infinity).

We've already met a singularity like this in the previous chapter when we talked about the dripping tap and the period doubling route to chaos. You will remember that as we gradually turn the tap on, the period of the dripping doubles from one ('drip'...'drip'...'drip'), to two ('drip'-'drip'...'drip'-'drip') and then four, and so on. Thus a small change in one quantity (the volume of water coming out of the tap) results in a large change in the period of the dripping. Then there comes a point at which the period of the drips goes to infinity (= chaos). This is a singularity. Each time the period doubles, the dripping tap exhibits a singularity until it reaches a infinite dripping period, which is full-blown chaos. Actually, singularities are very common in chaotic systems in general. A point that we will come back to later in this chapter.

8.2. The Technological Singularity

This concept of a singularity was first applied to technological progress by the father of the modern computer John von Neumann. In his tribute to von Neuman in a 1958 edition of the Bulletin of the American Mathematical Society, Polish scientist Stanislaw Ulam recalled a conversation in which von Neumann described the relationship between accelerating technological progress and changes in the mode of human life. He predicted that there would come a point in this progress, which he described as a singularity, after which human "affairs, as we know them, could not continue." This concept of the technological singularity has been used by a number of authors since then, including science fiction author Vernor Vinge who published an essay in 1993 entitled 'The Coming Technological Singularity'. The essay described how super-intelligence would ultimately bring the end of the human race.

What is the basis for these alarming predictions and what evidence do these prophets of doom have for spreading them? There are two underlying aspects to this which on the face of it make these extreme predictions seem plausible: Increasing computational capacity, and the ability of AI systems to self learn.

Increasing computational capacity

In his book, 'The Singularity is Near', the futurist and inventor Ray Kurzweil presents credible evidence for the exponential growth in technological progress. He starts right back at the dawn of life on earth, tracking the evolutionary development of humans alongside the development of technologies. He begins with art and writing, the wheel, electricity, and moves along the time line to the computer; each development appearing in a shorter time than the previous, showing signs of exponential rate of growth in technologies. He also reflects on the development of computer technologies in more recent times, plotting progress from 1900 onwards through the 20th century, from the electromechanical instrumentation of the early 20th century to the development of the integrated circuit towards the end of that century. The rate of development across that period is measured in the number of calculations a computing device can perform per second. Based on *Moore's law*, this progress follows not an exponential curve, but an 'S' shaped curve.

In 1965 Gordan Moore, who worked on the development of the integrated circuit and who later became founder and chairman of Intel Corporation, made a prediction in an issue of the magazine Electronics, that the number of transistors (fundamental building blocks of electronics) on integrated circuits would double every year over the following ten year period. In 1975 he revised his prediction to a doubling every two years. His predictions took into account advancements in manufacturing technology used to create integrated circuits and the subsequent progressive reductions in production costs. His prediction turned out to be quite accurate and later became known as Moore's Law. Technology manufacturers used Moore's law to inform their long term planning, setting future product developments that would line up with the predicted numbers of transistors on individual chips. So, in effect, Moore's predictions became a self-fulfilling prophecy.

This doubling in the number of transistors on integrated circuits every two years corresponded to an exponential increase in device complexity, which resulted in an increase in the computation power that the device could support. In the last 10 years the rate of increase in chip complexity has slowed to doubling every 2.5 years. The number of transistors that can be squeezed on to a chip per unit area is now approaching physical limits and manufacturers are exploring other ways of increasing chip complexity and compactness. These limits to this exponential growth in complexity of current forms of integrated circuit technology imply that this is following an 'S' curve, rather than an exponential curve, since the top end of the curve, which corresponds to the slow down of the growth, flattens out.

Kurzweil points out, however, that integrated circuits are only the latest of five technological paradigms. Beginning with Electromechanical circuits at the turn of the 20th Century, Kurzwell shows that each of these paradigms exhibited exponential growth in the number of calculations per second per $1,000 until they were replaced by subsequent paradigms. Following the electromechanical paradigm were a relatively short period of relay-based devices, then vacuum tubes, then transistors, leading onto integrated circuit technology. Kurzweil predicted, back in 2005, that Moore's Law for transistor based technologies would reach the end of its 'S' curve by 2020, and that the exponential growth in computation power will be continued by a new paradigm based on 3-D molecular computing. Though his predicted end of Moore's Law has not occurred yet, it is clear that it will come to an end in the near future. The next paradigm has not yet materialised, but the industry is looking at technologies that do not depend on physical scaling to produce increases in computational power.

The point that Kurzweil was making in his predictions, however, was that the forces that cause these increases in the rate of technological growth are much broader than the capacity to produce increasingly complex and compact devices. He argues that what is really driving these advancements is what he calls the "law of accelerating returns". This is based on the observation that many evolutionary processes tend to increase at exponential rates, with increasingly complex life forms developing within increasingly shorter time scales. He also observes that the complexity and rate of development of the outputs or products of an evolutionary process increases at an exponential rate.

This includes technological development. He argues that the

technological singularity is an inevitable result of the law of accelerating returns, predicting that this will occur before the end of the 21st Century. In fact, he postulated, based on the trends he observes in technology development, that it will take place around 2045.

Kurzweil bases this prediction of the coming technological singularity on a list of 37 principles which he describes in quite some detail in his book. Here we shall pull out a couple of these and offer a perspective on their potential contribution to the occurrence of the technological singularity.

One of Kurzweil's principles is based on the fact that the technology behind human brain scanning is advancing significantly, with both spatial and temporal resolution doubling every year (at least up to the time of him writing that). The inevitable outcome, he argues, is that within two decades we will have a detailed understanding of the workings of all the regions of the brain. At the time of writing this, we find ourselves over three quarters of the way through those two decades, and we are still far from being able to describe with any certainty how every region of the brain works. There have, of course, been many helpful discoveries over that period, and neuroscience has clearly advanced significantly. But there are still many key questions about the human brain that remain to be answered.

We should take a moment to reflect on the proposal that if we acquired complete knowledge of the physical structure of the brain and its temporal neural activity, then we would be able to recreate all of that in sufficient detail with a machine that was capable of matching the brain's cognitive abilities. It is one thing to have a 3D temporal and structural recording of neural activity, it is quite another to build a physical device that would replicate it, and more than that, exceed the performance of the brain itself. Nevertheless, in recent years significant amounts of public funding has been pumped into projects that seek this ambitious aim. Our present discussion about the technological singularity will be assisted by taking a look at the work being done in this area, beginning with the humble Artificial Neural Network.

The biggest advancements in Artificial Intelligence over the last 10 years has been made possible through a technology that is inspired by the micro-structure of the brain: Artificial Neural Networks (ANNs). ANNs consist of software objects that broadly correspond to biological neurons. These simulated neurons are actually very simple devices that take as input the (weighted) signals (expressed as numbers) from other artificial neurons, and then apply a simple mathematical function (e.g. a threshold) to decide what the output of the neuron will be. This output is then passed on to other neurons in the network.

These artificial neurons are like light switches – some of them are on-off type switches, others are more like dimmer switches, producing an output that is proportional to the input that is received (Figure 8.2). Before the output of one neuron is passed onto another neuron, it is multiplied by a positive or negative number (weight). These positive and negative weights model the excitation and inhibiting influence that one biological neuron can have on another in the

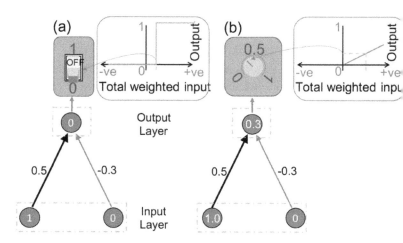

Figure 8.2: Two types of artificial neurons: (a) ones that produce binary outputs, and (b) ones that produces outputs on a continuous, bounded scale.

brain. Learning in these ANN models is achieved by modifying these weights.

It is worth highlighting that each of these artificial neurons has a very simple representation of its state of activation, often just a static, single real number. And that the means with which it communicates that limited state to other neurons to which it is connected is also extremely limited; normally represented either by a binary value (0 = not active, 1 = active), or a value in the range of 0 to 1, or similar.

Variations of these ANN models are created by choosing different structures in the network, such as the number of layers of neurons, and by choosing how neurons in one layer are connected to neurons in another layer. The recent successes of ANN models has largely been secured by increasing the number of layers of these networks, creating what are now call *deep neural networks*. These networks often have huge numbers of weights ('parameters') that have to be adjusted to enable them to learn the task at hand. The image recognition deep neural network AlexNet, for example, had 60 million weights. The more recently developed Generative Pre-trained Transformer 3 (GPT-3) for natural language processing has in the order of 175 billion weights. Training such large networks requires extraordinary amounts of compute power which has only relatively recently become available.

Despite their overall size and complexity, these deep neural network models do not come anywhere near close to the structural and operational complexity of the human brain. Biological neurons are significantly more complex than their artificial correlates, each containing many thousands of processes that occur both within the cell body and in the cell's extensions (dendrites and axons). Furthermore, these internal neuronal process interact with each other, giving rise to complex internal dynamics which drive the behaviour of the neuron and the networks to which it is connected. This low level complexity at the microscopic level gives rise to higher order complexity at region and whole brain levels, enabling the brain to function efficiently and effectively at high level cognitive tasks, consuming only 20 Watts of power to achieve this. In contrast, lower bound power consumption estimates of GPT-3 are in the order of 500MWh.

The most significant difference between the compute power of artificial and biological neuronal networks stems from two factors. The first is that information in artificial neural networks tends to pass through all neurons in all layers, requiring the multiplication of extremely large collections of numeric values in the form of vectors and matrices. Biological neural networks, on the other hand, are event driven: information is passed between specific groups of neurons using timed spike events, which is much more efficient and scalable than matrix multiplication. The second factor that influences compute power is the fact that artificial neural networks represent information in static numeric values, whereas biological neuronal networks represent and process information through dynamic processes, which offers a much richer computational framework.

A second principle in Kurzweil's list that he claims con- tributes to the inevitability of the technical singularity concerns brain implants. Brain implants consist of devices that connect physically to the brain and which can stimulate and/or read the activity of the neurons close to the device. The primary uses of these devices are to support the treatment of or to compensate for brain damage to particular areas of the brain following a stroke or brain injury. These devices are also being used to create brain-computer-interface technologies, where the device gathers data about the activity of neurons in the brain associated with particular thoughts. Pattern recognition techniques can then be used to recognise the neural signals and associate them with the thought that generated them. This can then be used to enable thought-control of objects such as robots.

Kurzweil's concern is that the computational capacity of these brain implants will increase at a much faster rate than the corresponding capacity of the brain, and consequently dominating and overpowering the intelligence of the brain. Fifteen years after raising these concerns, there is no sign of anything of the sort taking place. The technology is able to enhance perceptual capabilities, sometimes restoring sensory data such as vision which had been lost due to brain damage. But there is no evidence to date of the technology becoming even remotely as close to intelligent as its host. There are other genuine ethical concerns about these devices, such as privacy and security of data transmission from the device, but the devices themselves have yet to demonstrate anything to substantiate Kurzweil's concerns.

These and many other arguments in support of the technological singularity are founded on the comparison of human intelligence with some future computer-based super intelligence. Typically, this argument goes something like this: computers can already outperform humans in a number of cognitive tasks, and, given the increasing pace of technological development, it is inevitable that there will come a time when they will outperform humans in all areas of cognitive competence. One way of illustrating this inevitability that is used by some of the proponents of the technical singularity is shown in Figure 8.3. The inner patterned circle represents the full range of human cognitive abilities, with the distance from the centre representing the degree of cognitive competence humans possess to perform specific tasks. The circle segments or shards that extend beyond the inner circle represent the areas where machines currently outperform humans in specific tasks. The inevitability of the technological singularity is illustrated by observing that techno-

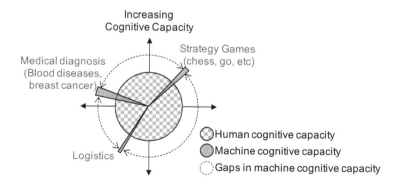

Figure 8.3: Human versus machine cognitive capacity.

logical advancement will enable machines to eventually and inevitably fill in the gaps between the shards.

Whilst it is true that computers can out-perform humans in some very specific areas (e.g. Alpha Go and Deep Blue each beating the world champion at their respective games), there are three underlying assumptions of the proposed gap filling route to 'super-intelligence' that need to be exposed.

The first assumption is that machines will inevitably be able to out-perform humans in all aspects of their cognitive capacity. To put this assumption into perspective, it should be noted that in all of the cases we have seen so far of machines out-performing humans on cognitive tasks, the task itself has facilitated the use of the *computational* rather than *cognitive* advantage that machine have over humans. AlphaGo, for example, used a large game tree to anticipate and evaluate many more viable future move sequences than its human opponent ever could. This kind of cognitive task lends itself to superior algorithmic solutions. The same is true for other areas where large data sets or significant numbers of options have to be computed. This is what computers are particularly good at. But one cannot assume that all, or even a significant proportion of cognitive tasks that humans perform well will afford this kind of computational advantage.

The second key assumption of the 'gap-filling' route to the technological singularity is that human cognitive capacity is bounded, fixed and slow to adapt relative to the speed of technological development. In Chapter 7 we explored the possibility of a limitless capacity of the human brain in terms of the number of different thoughts it could entertain if its underlying dynamics of were chaotically driven. Whilst there is no proof that the dynamics of the brain are chaotic, one cannot simply assume that human cognitive capacity is bounded, that the mind is constrained to a fixed number of thoughts and thought processes. This assumption underlies Kurzweil's claim that human cognitive capacity is slow to develop relative to the speed of technological advancement. In his argument he is referring to the physical development of the brain that takes place at a slow evolutionary pace. But this neglects the agility and adaptability of the mind of the individual that is already facilitated by their brain. The brain's structure does not need to keep pace with technological development for it to outperform machine intelligence on a broad range of cognitive tasks.

The third, and perhaps most significant assumption that underlies the 'gap-filling' route to the technological singularity relates to human versus machine autonomy. The ability to think and act freely and independently is a fundamental facet of human cognitive capacity. It is the source of human creativity and originality which enables us to develop new ways of thinking and acting within the world. As we saw in Chapter 7, machine autonomy is subject to the limits of physical causation and is consequently very limited in comparison to human freewill. Cognitive autonomy is a gap that will never be filled by intelligent machines.

Although Kurzweil's arguments for the technological singularity have been very influential, there has been a good deal of criticism not just of his assumptions, but also of his approach. Notably, Theodore Modis, who's work on accelerating technological change informed many of Kurzweil's claims, has been highly critical of Kurzweil's work and the way in which he develops his arguments, saying that they lacked scientific rigour.

Self-Adaptation

But Kurzweil and others are not just concerned about rapid increases in computational power, they are also worried about the ability of AI systems to learn and improve themselves. This capacity for 'self-adaptation' was introduced to Artificial Intelligence solutions around the turn of the century to help deal with the increasing complexity of computing systems. It has since become one of the primary ways of enabling a system to rapidly learn to solve tasks in highly complex problem domains. Self-adaptation is achieved by providing the system with a feedback signal through which it can evaluate and enhance its own performance. It has been particularly successful in rapidly enhancing the performance of game playing AI systems where the feedback comes from the system playing against itself. The most notable recent success in this arena is AlphaGo, which is often cited as an example of the self-adaptive route to the technological singularity.

It is important to have a clear understanding of how Alpha Go learned to improve its game playing in order to put self-adaptation into perspective. DeepMind, who were the creators of Alpha-Go, used a combination of AI technologies to develop the system. As we saw earlier, its core was formed by classical game-theory tree searching where the nodes on the tree typically correspond to board positions, and the branches coming from it are the possible moves that a player could take from that position. This enables the program to look ahead and try to predict and evaluate future moves following the next move of the program. In a game like Go, the numbers of possible moves grows very quickly, and there is a need to prune the tree and focus the software's attention on positions of higher value in the game. The programme uses machine learning to learn the value of board positions and moves which are then used to guide the tree search.

The learning process began by getting the programme to copy the moves of human expert players that were stored in a large database. Its competence at playing was then enhanced through self-adaptation by getting the programme to play against previous versions of itself, learning to improve through a reward based system. After a significant number of games against itself it had reached a sufficient level of competence to challenge the top players at Go. A professional Go player call Fan Hui was hired to play against AlphaGo to test the program's competence. Then in 2016 Fan Hui was appointed as one of the judges of the competition in which AlphaGo beat Lee Sedol.

You may recall from our earlier discussion of this competition Fan Hui's response to the now famous 37th move of AlphaGo in the second game against Sedol. "So beautiful" he kept saying. This s tory hit the world headlines and has been repeated numerous times to illustrate the potential for super human machine intelligence. But at this point it is worth noticing that although Fan Hui saw the beauty of that 37th move, AlphaGo didn't. It had no appreciation whatsoever of how smart or surprising or "super intelligent" that move was. It doesn't have the capacity to appreciate the value of any of the moves that it made. The reason it doesn't have that capacity is that it is an algorithm that has been designed to optimise a mathematical function based on the feedback it receives. The algorithm has no idea that its operations and "decisions" are controlling a game called Go. It had no understanding of its human opponent Lee Sedol. Impressive though this artificial intelligence is, it is a disconnected kind of intelligence, it is disconnected from the real world in which it operates. This is because self-adaptation of this kind is highly focussed on one task and one task alone and is not sufficient in and of itself to lead to the much feared technological singularity.

8.3. The Creational Singularity

Arguments for the inevitability of the technological singularity tend to grossly over estimate the abilities of AI algorithms and grossly underestimate the capabilities of human beings. Most of these arguments focus much more on the emerging capabilities of AI powered systems than they do on the remarkable abilities that humans already possess. We seem to have lost sight of how "fearfully and wonderfully" we are made. In fact, I would venture to argue that the existence of human beings within the universe already constitutes a *creational* singularity both from a biological and a spiritual point of view. I propose that two particular aspects of humanity support this claim: cognitive complexity and personhood.

Cognitive complexity

There are significant biological differences between humans and other creatures in this world. Whilst we share many common features with other mammals in terms of our low level micro-biology (cell structure, connectivity, etc.), and our high level biological structures (muscular-skeletal structures, blood ves- sels, major organs etc.), there are notable differences and the majority of these are in the brain.

The human brain has some quite distinct features which are not found in other mammals. The first is that our brains are very large for our body size and the extra volume is mostly found in the cortex which supports the high level cognitive abilities such as language, problem solving and self awareness, that make humans very different to other creatures.

In addition to its size, there are other significant differences in human brains that make them unique in the mammalian kingdom. The first is that there is a greater number of neurons in the *association cortex*. These are cortical regions that are found between auditory, visual and somatosensory regions of the cortex that have the task of integrating the sensory signals that emerge from those areas. Furthermore, human brains have a larger number of neuron fibres than are found in other primates. The human brain also has different patterns of gene expression to other mammals, which has an effect on how the brain develops and makes connections as it matures from childhood to a full grown adult brain.

Combined together, these biological differences in the brain do make humans quite distinct as creatures in this world. But I would suggest that these physiological differences have resulted in an exponential increase in the functional capacity of the human brain that facilitates the extraordinary high level cognitive abilities that make us unique in all of creation.

Let me unpack this a little to show how this is possible. Starting first with the increase in neurons in the association layers. Recent

work in AI has demonstrated that certain types of pattern association artificial neural networks (Hopfield recurrent neural networks)
have an exponential relationship between the number of neurons
in the network and the maximum number of patterns it can store.
So, in other words, each additional neuron to a pattern association
network increases the number of patterns the network can store by
an *increasing* amount. If this factor is also true of the human brain,
which inspired the design of these artificial neural networks, then
human capacity to remember the associations it forms between the
patterns of activation in different sensory regions will likely be hugely
more powerful in humans than the other primates. The additional neuron fibres will also have a considerable influence on memory
capacity since the terminals of these fibres, the synapses, are one of
the primary supports of memory storage in the brain.

But these increases in processing capacity could be even more
significant if the underlying dynamics of the brain are chaotic,
as we explored in Chapter 7. Increases in both the number of neurons and the number of neuron fibres has the potential to significantly increase the complexity of the chaotic attractors that support
memory storage and recall. This could, in turn, substantially increase
the information processing capacity of the brain. If all this is true,
then from an evolutionary biology perspective, the relatively recent
development of the human brain has resulted in a significant spike
in high level cognitive performance that is far greater than that found
in other species and that resembles a kind of singularity in itself.

Personhood

Beyond this evolutionary biology perspective, there is a deeper
sense in which the human species constitutes a kind of singularity,
and that is related to their identity as persons. From a theological
perspective, each human is a unique person, an *individual singularity*
emerging from a combined biological and spiritual reality, fearfully
and wonderfully made. For many people, this is the key differentiator

not just between humans and animals, but between humans and any artificial agent created by humans.

Our Western understanding of 'personhood' has emerged from a long and complex history with roots in both Hebrew theology and Greek philosophy and is intimately entwined with the concept of the 'self'[2]. The theological roots of personhood come from expressions of individuals (e.g. God, humans) being in relationship with each other. The Hebrew concept of person is different from the Greek in that it attributed significance to the individual, each being made in God's image, and to the understanding that personhood is what binds us together as human beings. From a Christian theology perspective, these relationships are spiritual. God is Spirit, and each human has a spirit.

We have briefly considered how the appearance of the human race might be viewed as a singularity from a evolutionary biology perspective, but it is interesting to also look at it from a theological perspective through the lens of the creation story in Genesis. Note the sequence of days (or 'epochs' if you prefer) in the creation story:

- Day 1: Light (day and night)

- Day 2: Sky

- Day 3: Land and seas, vegitation

- Day 4: Sun, moon and stars

- Day 5: Living creatures in water and sky

- Day 6: Living creatures on land, then mankind, created in God's image.

If one could measure complexity in creation on each of these days,

[2]Stephen Millford, from an early draft of his PhD Thesis

it would likely show that the increase in complexity from day 2 to day 3 was greater than the increase in complexity from day 1 to day 2. Then there are even greater increases in complexity on days 4, 5 and 6, which culminated in the creation of the most complex biological objects on earth – human beings. This is the biological singularity that we've just been considering. But a closer look at scripture shows that something unique happened during the creation of Adam and Eve. In verse 7 of Genesis chapter 2, we read:

> "Then the Lord God formed a man from the dust of
> the ground and breathed into his nostrils the breath of
> life, and the man became a living being"

None of the other creatures were created in this way, only humans. But what is this actually saying about how humans were created and what is the significance of God breathing into the man the breath of life? What is the breath of life?

The most popular view in Jewish and Christian thought is that the "breath of life" is essentially endowing the man with a soul. Traditionally, the possession of a soul is what distinguishes human beings from the other creatures that God made. However, this is not exactly what the original Hebrew text says. One Hebrew commentary provides some helpful insight into three terms that are used in this verse in Genesis 2[3]. The first is the word that is translated as "formed", which in ancient Hebrew is normally spelled as רצי (vayyitzer) using a single Yod, which is the tenth letter of the Hebrew alphabet and looks a bit like an apostrophe:י. In the Hebrew Bible this word vayyitzer occurs 19 times. In only one of these is the word spelled with two Yods:רצ"ו which is in this verse in chapter 2 of Genesis. The commentary goes on to highlight the significance of this (emphasis is mine):

> "It turns out that two Yods (יי) is a form of the inef-
> fable name of God. The ancient Hebrews interpreted

[3]Learn Biblical Hebrew, http://learn-biblical-hebrew.com/hebrew-scripture/garden-of-eden-story/genesis-27/ (accessed 06/07/2021)

> the deliberate addition of the second Yod to express, in
> literary form, that God endowed mankind with a spe-
> cial and absolutely unique ability — the ability to act
> in ways counter to our natural instincts. Humans stand
> alone in having the ability to rise above their natural,
> animal inclinations."

This ability to act in ways that are counter to our natural instincts is, I believe, absolutely key to our capacity to be moral agents. Recall that this is one of the action focussed criteria for moral agency that we identified in Chapter 1: a capacity to rise above feelings and passions and act according to moral law (A3). In terms of the moral agent architecture we discussed in Chapter 6, the so called natural instincts are the default behaviours that emerge from the pursuit of our needs and desires. What is it in that architecture that enables us to rise above these? It is the Executive Centre, or in theological terms, it is the spirit of the person, which is deeply connected to the brain, but which goes far beyond the causal determinism that would constrain a person into following their 'natural inclinations', as we discussed in Chapter 7.

So does this 'breath of life' concept corresponds more to the imbuing of a person's spirit than it does their soul? There are some commentators that think so. One comments that the phrase 'breath of life' in Hebrew is נשׁיתמ (nishmat chayyim), but the word that is commonly translated to 'spirit' in English is חור (ruach)[4]. Whilst in Genesis 2:7 the phrase *nishmat chayyim* is used to describe what God breathed into man through his nostrils, we see that in Genesis chapter 7, after describing the onset of the flood, verses 21-22 say the following:

> "Every living thing that moved on land perished -
> birds, livestock, wild animals, all the creatures that
> swarm over the earth, and all mankind. Everything on

---

[4]https://hermeneutics.stackexchange.com/questions/2739/is-breath-of-life-in-genesis-27-is-the-same-as-spirit, Biblical Hermeneurtics (accessed 06/07/2021)

dry land that had the breath of life in its nostrils died."

Here, the phrase "breath of life" includes ruach in the middle: בִּשְׁתַּם חוּר יּחַ (nishmat ruach chayyim), which this commentator takes as a strong indication that the term "breath of life" is equivalent to "spirit".

How is this relevant to our discussion on the personal singularity? It is relevant because the imbuing of the human with spirit is core to the theological understanding of personhood, and provides us with the capacity to rise above our natural instincts and be moral agents. We have the capacity to be moral agents because God has imbued us with a spirit. This places humans in a unique category in all of creation and as such constitutes another kind of singularity: the personal singularity. But it does much more than that. It is a personal singularity also in that the imbuing of a spirit enables each of us to be unique, individual creations.

If there is to be a moral singularity at all, it has already taken place. Human beings constitute a moral singularity who, by virtue of the spirit that is within them, rise significantly above and beyond the natural order and have the freedom to choose between morally good and morally bad actions. They have a capacity for highly creative acts that is far above anything that can be done by God's other earthly creatures. And personhood is itself a kind of singularity that is repeated in the birth, growth and development of every individual human being.

All of this is only possible because of a creator God, who is himself far above and beyond the universe that he created. Human being are made in his image, and so reflect something of the greatness of God in their potential for creating great good.

It may be the case that machines will be developed that exceed human capacity in a number of areas relating to our cognitive abilities. But I hope this chapter has helped to show that the occurrence of the technical singularity that is feared, and the associated moral singularity, are both highly improbable. In my view, no artificial intelligence algorithm will ever have the power of the spirit that is within human beings that enables them to rise above their natural inclinations and act in ways that are consistently intelligent, creative and moral.

Time will tell, of course. But we are barely at the knee of the exponential curve we are following when it comes to reproducing or replicating human intelligence and cognitive capacity. There will, of course, be many simulations of this cognitive capacity that might tempt us to think that these machines have risen beyond general human capacity in this respect. And at some point we may not even be able to tell the difference between the simulated and the genuine human. How should we respond to this? That is the topic we turn to in the next and final chapter.

Chapter 9
I COMPUTE, THEREFORE I AM

In 1969 President Nixon's speech writer William Safire prepared a speech for Nixon to read in the event that the Apollo 11 moon landing ended in disaster that July. As we know, the landing was successful, Neil Armstrong and Buzz Aldrin were not stranded on the moon, and Nixon didn't give the 'In Event of Moon Disaster' speech. Just over half a century later, however, a video of Nixon apparently giving the moon disaster speech was published online.

The video was the work of Francesca Panetta and Halsey Burgund who are media artists at the Massechusetts Institute of Technology. The artists worked with two AI companies to create a 'deepfake' video of the speech that Nixon never gave. It is interesting to note that although the creators of this video were clear from the outset that this was a fake, there are some who were convinced that this really was a video of Nixon giving that speech.

There is no doubt that artificial intelligence technology is enabling us to create evermore realistic simulations of humans. The boundary between the simulated and the real is beginning to blur. Now more than ever, we need to reflect deeply on the impact that this blurring of boundaries will bring, especially when those boundaries are concern with the moral agency of humans and machines. We will return to the issue of 'deepfakes' later in this chapter, but first we need to review the criteria for moral agency that we identified in Chapter 1 in the light of all that we have discussed in the meantime.

9.1. Robot Moral Agency

You will recall that our list of criteria for moral agency was drawn from both philosophical and theological sources and that they were divided into the following four groups based on the context in which they are applied: Action focussed, inner life focussed, personhood focussed, and community focussed. Let's review where we are with each of these in turn.

		Capacity to:
Action	A1	act according to moral standards
Focused	A2	act altruistically
	A3	rise above feelings and passions and act according to moral law

Table 9.1: Action focused criteria for possessing moral agency

Action

The capacity to act within the world is fundamental to the notion of *agency*: an entity that cannot act does not possess agency. And so the first of our criteria in Table 9.1 (A1) identifies the lowest bar that robots would need to reach in order to be credited with moral agency. They have to be able to act in the world according to moral standards. We are well aware that robots have the capacity to act within the world - that's what makes them useful to us. The extent to which we can programme our robots to perform these acts in accordance with moral standards determines the level of moral agency our robots will reach.

Recall that in Chapter 3 we introduced three levels of moral agency, which, going from the lowest to the highest, were: operational morality, functional morality and full moral agency. Almost all commercially available robots are designed to conform to safety standards that minimise the physical harm they can cause through their actions. Some are also designed to implicitly conform to other aspects of moral behaviour, for example, by being truthful in their speech and by not acting with deliberate evil intent. These robots do succeed in achieving a degree of moral agency at the operational level. The next two levels (functional morality and full-moral agency) seem to require more than just the ability to act in the world. We will return to these as we consider the inner life criteria for moral agency.

The ability to act altruistically (A2) goes beyond merely acting according to moral standards. The Oxford English Dictionary defines 'altruism' as: "Devotion to the welfare of others, regard for others, as a principle of action; opposed to egoism or selfishness". Whilst robots don't normally embody egoism or selfishness, that doesn't make them altruistic by default. This 'devotion to the welfare of others' needs to be coded into the software that drives the behaviour of the robot. Much like the virtue of kindness exhibited by our groceries delivery robot in Chapter 6, the robot has to actively seek out opportunities to work for the good of others. This is not trivial from a technical point of view, but nevertheless, it seems potentially achievable once we have developed algorithms with this level of sophistication.

The third capacity in our action focussed list of criteria requires that our moral robots rise above their feelings and passions and act according to moral law (A3). You will recall that this was generally regarded as the strongest of the requirements emerging from the philosophical debate on this topic. The difficulty with this one is that whilst emotions are innate in humans they are non-existent in robots. Whilst it is true that endowing robots with emotions is an active research agenda pursued by roboticists, these will be simulations of emotions at best. It seems a bit contrived to first give robots emotions and then expect them to learn how to rise above them to act according to moral law.

As we saw in the previous chapter, this ability of humans rise above their feelings and passions and act according to moral law is tied closely to the theological view of personhood and the God-breathed spirit that distinguishes humans from all other earthly creatures. It seems that, from this perspective at least, robots will never have the capacity to meet criteria A3.

	IL1	Possess an enduring, conscious, inner life
Inner life Focused	IL2	Awareness of moral obligations and an ability to discern right from wrong
	IL3	Possess (libertarian) free will
	IL4	Ability to reflect on own moral actions and condition

Table 9.2: Inner life criteria for possessing moral agency

Inner Life

The Inner life focussed criteria are much more demanding from a moral machine perspective than the action based criteria because they presume the existence of an inner, conscious thought life that is the source of the agent's actions (IL1, Table 9.2).

This begs the question as to whether machines are capable of conscious thought of the kind presumed by these criteria.

The title of this chapter is intended to draw attention to this question. It is an adaptation of the well-known phrase that was penned by Rene Descartes in his book *Discourse on the Method*:

"Cogito, ergo sum" ("I think, therefore I am"). Descartes used this phrase to support his claim for *personal existence* in a world where our senses, imagination and dreams can deceive us about reality and even cause us to doubt our own existence. He claimed that "we cannot doubt our existence while we doubt". In other words, you have to exist in order to doubt. More than that, you have to be a conscious being capable of thought. More than that even, you have to be aware that you are the *source* of the doubting thought.

There is a good deal of criticism of Descartes' method of arriving at this conclusion, which we shall have to bypass here as it will divert us too much from our present discussion. The phrase "I compute, therefore I am", however, should cause us to pause and reflect on our assumptions about *computation* and question whether it leads to the kind of self-awareness and conscious thought that meet the requirements of the inner life criteria.

Our understanding of the activity of thinking has changed considerably in recent years with the advent of the computer. We have arrived at a place where many people regard thinking as very much like the operations that go on inside a computer. A computer program is, after all, itself an expression of thought, coded in logical form, and consisting of sequences of explicit instructions that manipulate data, solve problems, an even control events in the world beyond the computer. All of this sounds pretty much like thinking in many ways.

This view that thought is a kind of computation was first suggested by Thomas Hobbes in his book 'On the Body' in 1655. Writing long before the advent of the modern computer, Hobbes asserted that computation can be understood through reasoning, and just as computation is an arithmetic process of summing many things together, reasoning can also be viewed as engaging similar arithmetic processes. Hobbs was far ahead of his time, and it took a further three hundred years for the *Computational Theory of Mind*, or 'Computationalism', to emerge in the middle of the 20th century as a recognised branch of philosophy.

Computationalism holds that the mind is an information pro-cessing system, and therefore that thought *is* a kind of computation. The problem for us with this view is that all forms of computation, including quantum computation, are deterministic. The repeated application of a set of computational processes to a given start state will always produce the same end state, each and every time. As we discussed in Chapter 7, this leaves no room for what we commonly understand as free will or autonomy in human beings, a property that is regarded by many philosophers to be an essential criteria for moral agency (IL3).

The Computational Theory of Mind still has a good deal of sup-port amongst philosophers today, but other competing paradigms of the mind have recently emerged including the view that the mind is a *dynamical system* rather than a computational one. The dynamical systems perspective includes the view that the brain (and hence the mind) is driven by the dynamics of chaos, as we explored in Chapter 7. But, as we have seen, chaos is also deterministic and if the human mind is driven by chaotic dynamics alone, then that too leaves no room for humans to meet criteria IL3, let alone machines.

In reality, computation is a poor analogy for thinking. They are very different kinds of things. Computation is strictly algorithmic, sequential and deterministic in nature. Conscious thought, on the other hand, doesn't appear to be constrained in this way. Or at least we don't experience it in those terms. But there is one aspect of thinking which stands out in comparison to computation, and that is *consciousness*. The statement "I think, therefore I am" assumes that it is a conscious individual that is having that thought. Conscious awareness seems to be fundamental to what it means to have a thought. Computation, on the other hand, does not require any form of consciousness, not even simulated consciousness.

Consciousness is extremely difficult to define. Philosophers have disagreed about how to define it for centuries. Even today, there is still no consensus on what consciousness is, except that it exists. At a basic level, consciousness involves a degree of awareness of interior or exterior phenomena. It involves a range of psychological and experiential things such as sensations, thoughts, emotions, and perceptions. The Cambridge English Dictionary defines consciousness as "the state of understanding and realizing something". I struggle with this one, because we can be conscious of things we don't understand (how many of us understand, I mean really understand quantum physics? And yet we can be conscious of it).

Where does consciousness come from? Consciousness does not appear to be a property of matter. There is no doubt that consciousness and matter are integrated in some deeply causal manner, with brain states causing mental states and visa versa[1]. But this causal relationship is entirely unique within the whole of the natural order: No matter other than brain tissue has this privileged association with consciousness. Furthermore, consciousness does not seem to be a permanent property owned by brain tissue, since brain tissue can exist dead or alive (i.e. live but unconscious) without any apparent associated conscious phenomena.

Neither can it be argued convincingly that consciousness exists in the *behaviour* of matter. What is it about the flow of ions across the membrane of a nerve cell that could make consciousness, whilst the flow of ions in a battery does not? How can the movements of neurotransmitters across synaptic junctions induce conscious phenomena when the movements of the very same biochemicals in a vat do not? The probability that consciousness is a property of matter reduces even further when it is considered that the measurements that are applied to matter (length, weight, mass, etc.) cannot be applied to consciousness[2]. Neither can many qualities of consciousness be applied to matter, including sensory occurrences such as the redness of a rose, or the taste of coffee (i.e. 'Qualia'), or the fact that the owner of a conscious state has infallible first-person knowledge of that state by way of personal experience, or that consciousness endows the owner with freedom of choice (contrasted with the deterministic behaviour of matter), rational capabilities and self-awareness[3]. Given all of these distinctions, it seems extremely improbable that

[1]Swinburne (2004 pp195 and 196); McGinn (1997 p17)
[2]Swinburne (2004 p204)
[3]Mackie (1982 p122), Swinburne (2004 p193), McGinn (1997 p17)

consciousness is a property of matter.

If it is the case that consciousness is not a property of matter, what is it a property of? A theological perspective would postulate that consciousness is a property of the spirit of a person. God is a conscious being, and as Jesus said in John 4:24, "God is Spirit, and His worshippers must worship Him in spirit and truth". God does not depend on matter for his consciousness; He has neither body nor brain. Neither does he have a soul, as far as we know from the Bible. Remember that the function of the soul is to integrate all of the dimensions of the self together to form one individual. But since God doesn't have a body, he has no need for a soul. And yet he exhibits all of the properties that we have come to associate with a conscious, thinking being: he appears to experience emotions such as anger and joy, he exhibits an awareness of both interior and exterior phenomena, he is aware of himself, and so on.

The Biblical perspective of human beings is that they also have a spirit. You will recall that we have already discussed the relationship between the body and spirit in Chapter 7, a relationship in which the causal determinism of the brain interacts with the non-physical spirit to facilitate human autonomy and free will. Here we add to this claim that the spirit of a person is the seat of consciousness that integrates with the operations of the brain and together they form the mind of the person that can truly say "I think, therefore I am".

There is much more to say about consciousness than we are able to include here. But what should already be clear is that, according to the theological perspective we've just considered, machines do not have the ability for *conscious* thought or free will as humans experience it, and so are unable to meet two of the inner life focussed criteria for moral agency: IL1 - Possess an enduring, conscious, inner life, and IL3 - Possess (libertarian) free will.

It is arguable whether the remaining two criteria could, in principle, be met by the appropriately equipped machine. We have already described some machines that have the ability to discern right from wrong (IL2). In Chapter 4 we presented a number of systems that used either top-down or bottom-up approaches to developing machines with moral competence. The case for machines possessing the ability to reflect on their own moral actions and condition (IL4), however, is less clear. On the one hand, systems that have been given the ability to dis- cern right from wrong could apply that ability to themselves, observing their own behaviours and forming a judgement as to their moral rectitude. The capacity to *reflect*, though, implies a capacity for *conscious* deliberation, which we have already ruled out for machines.

Personhood

In Chapter 8 we discussed how personhood is commonly regard-ed as a unique attribute of humans within all of the natural order. Until very recently, it is an attribute that has not been routinely ap-plied to either animals or machines. The recent exception to this is the humanoid robot Sophia, who in 2017 was granted citizenship of Saudi Arabia and became first robot in the world to be given legal personhood status. Many have criticised this move from the Saudi Arabian authorities which has more of the appearance of a marketing stunt than a genuine recognition that Sophia possess the attributes required of personhood. That said, all four of the personshood fo-cussed criteria for moral agency that we identified in Chapter 1 seem largely attainable by robots (Table 9.3).

	Capacity for:	
Personhood	P1	embodiment
Focused	P2	character formation
	P3	cultural embedding
	P4	imitating moral models

Table 9.3: Personhood focused criteria for possessing moral agency

In Chapter 5 we discussed how the moral development of children was broadly aligned with the development of their bodies. At birth children are physically small and have very little direct control over their bodies, which limits the range of things they can actually do. As the child grows, their capacity for doing (morally good or bad) things expands, as does the range of their *embodied* experiences. The embodiment criteria for moral agency (P1) requires that the agent concerned be able to experience and act in the world through a bodily presence. Without a physical embodiment, the agent is not capable of doing anything which could be regarded as morally good or bad. It is important to note, though, that in the context of machines, this embodiment doesn't have to be through conventional robotic limbs and sensors. Algorithmic embodiment can take many forms, including the ability to search and create content on the internet. As with humans, the extent to which a machine can conform to, or violate, moral norms depends on the effective reach of its embodiment.

Character formation (P2) is a progressive, developmental process that goes hand in hand with a person's physical growth and maturity into adulthood. However, unlike physical growth, character formation does not stop when we become adults. Our character continues to be shaped by our experiences and the consequences of our decisions and actions throughout the remainder of our lives. Our character is also the primary source of our routine actions and responses and will tend to incline us towards or away from moral ways of behaving. Virtue, if we possess it at all, is an expression of character. In Chapter 6 we explored the possibility of enabling machines to acquire virtues like kindness. Whilst virtue has yet to be convincingly demonstrated in machines, the endowment of robots with spontaneous acts of kindness, generosity and patience seems not to be beyond the realms of possibility.

The cultural embedding of machines (P3) in society refers to not just to their existence in the everyday lives of people; food mixers and washing machines have existed and functioned for quite some time in the everyday lives of many people, but they are not culturally embedded in the manner that is anticipated in P3. Cultural embedding here refers to the capacity to *be* a social agent. It requires that moral agents have the capacity to be relational and interact in social contexts with other social beings. This is because many of our moral standards are framed in socio-cultural or relational terms (e.g. "Love your neighbour as yourself"). The social embedding of machines has already begun with the development of robots like Jibo, who functions much more like a social companion than a labour saving device. Turning now to the criteria that moral agents should have the capacity for imitating moral models (P4), we should note that teaching by demonstration is a method that is commonly used to enable robots to learn to perform complex tasks. These demonstrations can be done in different ways. One way is for the demonstrator or mentor to simply to take hold of the robot arm and guide it through the movements it needs to make in order to complete the task. Another way is for the robot to observe someone performing the task, and then attempt to complete the same task itself. The successful acquisition of the new skill by the robot often requires multiple demonstrations.

These new skills need not be restricted to manual tasks. They can also include other tasks such as learning to engage in a spoken conversation, or learning to recognise the symptoms of a disease. In fact the data that is used to train most machine learning applications comes from humans performing the tasks that we would like the machine to do. In Chapter 4 we discussed several systems that could apply this kind of learning to the development of moral capacity in robots. You may recall, for example, the system that learned normative descriptions of actions through the stories of the comic strip 'Goofus and Gallant', with Gallant effectively being the moral model that the robot was learning to imitate. There is, therefore, already evidence that robots can learn to imitate moral models (P4).

	Capacity for:	
Community Focused	C2	being in relationships with human beings
	P4	being in relationship with God

Table 9.4: Community focused criteria for possessing moral agency

Community

Almost all moral norms and standards are relational, defining good and bad ways of treating and interacting with others. In most cases, these norms and standards emerge from within communities and often become deeply embedded in their identity and culture. This is certainly true of the moral standards in Judeo-Christian communities as defined in the Torah and the teachings of Jesus; these standards effectively define what it means to be a Jew or a Christian. In John 13 Jesus said to his followers "A new command I give you: Love one another. As I have loved you, so you must love one another. By this everyone will know that you are my disciples, if you love one another" (my emphasis). The moral standard of loving each other as Jesus loved them is what will identify and differentiate his disciples from other people.

There is an expectation, therefore, that moral agents be capable of being relational, recognising and following community focused norms and standards. Our criteria for moral agency that were defined in Chapter 1 splits this requirement into two (Table 9.4): being in relationship with other human beings (C1) and being in relationship with God (C2). From a moral machine perspective C1 is, in principle, achievable. A good deal of research is being carried out in social robotics to enable machines to simulate the capacities required for them to engage in relationship-forming social interactions. This includes spoken interaction, bodily gestures and facial expressions. But the biggest factor in this relationship-forming endeavour is not the robot but the human and their tenancies to anthropomorphise machines, as we discussed in Chapter 3.

Humans have a habit of projecting human-like qualities onto other objects, be they cuddly toys, automobiles or humanoid robots. We talk to and interact with our digital devices as though they are conscious, human-like agents. A time will come when our digital devices will talk back and interact with us in ways which we will find engaging and relationship forming, even though they are just machines.

The second community focussed criteria for moral agency (C2), however, is a very different matter. Human beings are capable of being in relationship with God because they are created for that very purpose. As we discussed in Chapter 7, humans have dual citizenship; they are inhabitants of both heaven and earth, they have physical bodies and immaterial spirits. And it is this unique combination which enables them to be in relationship with God. Machines can have bodies that are human-like, but they will never have spirits. They will never have dual heaven-and-earth citizenship, and so will never be able to satisfy this criteria.

Overall, it seems that appropriately designed machines could meet some of the criteria for moral agency in each of our four categories, but by no means all of them. Of the three levels of moral capacity proposed by Wallach and Allen, machines could not reach full human-like moral agency as defined by the criteria we have set out, but they could certainly possess a degree of *functional* morality, enabling them to recognise and respond appropriately to ethically charged situations. Whilst genuine full moral agency may be out of reach of the machine, there is still the question of whether or not they would be able to *simulate* human behaviour well enough for us to be fooled into thinking that they possess human-like moral capacity. This takes us into the realm of high-fidelity simulations of humans, or 'deepfake humans'.

9.2. Deepfake Humans

> Sonny: "My father tried to teach me human emotions. They are . . . difficult"
>
> Spooner: "You mean your 'designer'". Sonny: "Yes"
>
> Spooner: "So why did you murder him?" Sonny: "I did not murder Dr Lanning"
>
> Spooner: "Want to explain why you were hiding at the crime scene?"
>
> Sonny: "I was frightened"
>
> Spooner: "Robots don't feel fear. They don't feel anything. They don't get hungry, they don't sleep . . . "
>
> Sonny: "I do. I have even had dreams"
>
> Spooner: "Human beings have dreams. Even dogs have dreams. But not you. You are just a machine. An imitation of Life"

(Extract from the film 'I Robot', 2004, Alex Proyas)

Like the short stories in this book, the movie I Robot is inspired by and based on the fictional stories of Isaac Asimov. Asimov set out to use these stories to raise some key questions about the relationship between humans and robots, focussing particularly on the moral behaviour of robots. The extract quoted above is taken from the scene in which detective Spooner is investigating what he believes to be the murder of Dr Lanning, the designer and creator of robots in the story.

You may have noticed the underlying incongruence in detective Spooner interrogation of Sonny. On the one hand he is telling Sonny that he is not a human being, he is merely an imitation of life. But on the other hand he is accusing him of murder – a crime that, up to now, could only be committed by a human being. This incongruence runs throughout the movie, with Spooner insisting that the robots should not be trusted and that they have a capacity for evil (i.e. that they have moral agency) even through in his view there is "nothing here, (gesturing to his heart), just lights and clockwork".

This incongruence is a common feature of many science fiction movies that include robots. The problem often raised in these stories relates to how we treat robots as they become increasingly autonomous, human-like and deeply embedded in society. The movie Blade Runner addresses this issue directly. In the original 1982 movie, and its sequel which was released in 2017, highly realistic humanoid robots called 'replicants' that are indistinguishable from humans in looks and behaviour, exist in off-world colonies and are illegal on earth. In the original movie, four of them escape and it is the job of the main protagonist (Deckard) to hunt these replicants down. Because replicants are highly realistic copies of humans, Deckard has to perform a special test on them to determine whether they are human or replicant.

This raises an interesting an challenging question: If there is no detectable difference between machine-based replicants and humans, does that mean that they truly are the same? A colleague of mine once said to me "If there is no objective test that can distinguish a robot from a human, then there is no difference between them". That comment challenged me to the core. I firmly believe that there are fundamental differences between humans and even highly realistic replicants or 'deepfake humans', but it is hard to articulate these under the conditions of an 'objective test'. In the remainder of this book, we will seek to develop a perspective on this.

Deepfakes

Deepfakes images or videos have generated considerable interest in the past few years. They are synthetically generated or modified using techniques from machine learning. The technology behind this is based on deep learning neural networks, hence they are named 'deepfakes'. Early on in the development of this technology, artificial intelligence algorithms such as Generative Adversarial Networks

(GANs) where trained on many images. The basic idea of the GAN is that it involves two components – a discriminator and a generator. The job of the discriminator is to correctly differentiate between genuine images of faces, and fake ones (a task similar to that of Deckard). The job of the generator is to create images that are good enough to fool the discriminator into thinking they are genuine images of faces.

At the start of the training, the generator is not very good at generating realistic images of faces, so the discriminator can easily learn the difference between the real and fake images. But as the generator learns how to generate convincing fake images, the discriminator gets better at spotting them. In effect, they compete against each other and as one improves, the other improves. After sufficient time the generator is capable of creating images that are very difficult for the discriminator to detect, and almost impossible for the human eye to recognise that these photo-realistic images are not real.

This technology has now been applied to videos where a real video of a person is edited so that the face of the person is replace by a deepfake image. The quality of these deepfake videos has reached an alarming level and has received much media attention. There is a deepfake of Tom Cruise doing a magic trick, for example, which was released on TikTok and posted to @deeptomcruise, which now has more than 380,000 followers worldwide. These deepfakes have understandably caused considerable concern. They can be used to create videos of people saying and doing things that are ethically questionable or politically impactful, and which they never actually said. In 2018, for example, a deepfake video was released which showed Barack Obama saying words he never uttered[4]. At one time we were commonly warned not to believe everything we read in a newspaper. We are now entering an age where people will say that about videos that appear online.

If this trend continues, then we may end up with deepfakes of humans in physical form, which could pose a number of ethical,

---

[4]14https://www.npr.org/2020/10/01/918223033/where-are-thedeep-fakes- in-this-presidential-election?t=1615186020340 (accessed 17/07/2021)

political and security challenges, as illustrated by the Deepfake Humans short story at the start of Part IV. We have already seen that significant progress has been made in this direction with the highly realistic Geminoid robots of Prof Hiroshi Ishiguro from Osaka university. More recently, Engineered Arts Ltd have created a commercially available humanoid robot called Ameca that exhibits a high degree of realism in mimicking human gestures and facial expressions[5]. There is no doubt in my mind that there will come a time when these robots could say and do things which might, for a moment at least, convince people that they are human beings, thereby making them eligible candidates for passing the so-called *Turing Test*.

In 1950, English mathematician and computer scientist Alan Turing published a paper entitled "Computing Machinery and Intelligence" in the journal Mind. In this paper he describes a test which he called the Imitation Game, later to become known as the Turing Test. The test was designed to evaluate whether or not an intelligent machine was indistinguishable from a human being. In the most common form of the test a human interrogator communicated with two other players through a text based system (e.g. teletype). One of the other players was a human and the third was a computer. The interrogator could ask questions of either of the other players, and would use this approach to arrive at a decision about which of the other players was human and which was computer. If the machine was intelligent enough, it should be indistinguishable from the human in the manner in which it answered the questions, and it would be deemed to have passed the test.

Since 2006, the Turing Test format has been used to award the annual Leobner Prize to the AI systems that are judged to be most human like. The chatbot Mitsuku has won the Leobner Prize 5 times in recent years, and holds the world record in terms of successes. Mitsuku is available on various online platforms to chat to the general public. The chatbot represents an 18 year old female from Leeds that has the ability to do some basic reasoning about what

[5]https://www.engineeredarts.co.uk/robot/ameca/ (accessed 14/07/2022)

people say to it and the questions they typically ask. If the technology behind Mitsuku was combined with Ishiguro's geminoids or Engineered Art's Ameca robot, then we would be heading towards some convincing deep-fake humans. At what point would we stop regarding them as machines and see them more equivalent to human beings? If they look and act as humans, then to all intent and purposes they are human, aren't they? A phrase that is commonly used to express this view is:

> "if it looks like a duck, swims like a duck and quacks like a duck, then it is a duck"

This phrase, which is attributed to the poet James Riley (1849-1916) and which later became known as the Duck Test, gets to the very heart of the issue we are addressing. If a robot looks like a human, talks like a human and walks like a human, then it is a human – right? Well, only if talking, walking and looking like a human constituted an exhaustive list of attributes that were collectively *essential* for being human. But actually no such exhaustive list of necessary properties exists. Furthermore, many of the most common attributes of humans are not possessed by some members of the species. The ability to walk, for example, is not an essential property of humans. Many humans are are unable to walk, including very young babies and paraplegics, but this does not cause us to doubt their humanity. The Duck Test appears not to support the conclusion that deefakes are, to all intents and purposes, human. So what are we to make of this 'objective test' argument raised by my colleague?

9.3. Authentically Human

There are two primary responses to the objective test argument. One is to note that it makes a fundamental category error, and the other is to frame it in the context of being *authentically human*. The objective test that my colleague referred is designed to reveal the difference between the behavioural or functional responses of two agents, one a robot the other a human (in the same way that the Turing Test does). So the conclusion from any such test can only be that either they are functionally or behaviourally the same or different. In other words the test supports a conclusion that is in the *functional* category. But to then to infer from this that there is no difference between the human and the robot (i.e. that they are in the same category) is drawing an *ontological* conclusion. You cannot draw an onto-logical conclusion from a test designed to distinguish functional characteristics[6].

The second response to this argument, and something which takes us to the core of what this book is about, focuses on the content of the argument, and specifically on the requirement of an *objective* test. Objective testing is good, scientific thinking. Scientists make every effort to be objective in how they test their hypotheses. But the kind of objective tests being described here are focussed on what can be manipulated and what is observable in the physical universe. If we accept the view that human beings are spirits with bodies, that we occupy a joint, deeply integrated heaven-and-earth reality, then objectives tests of this sort are going to have a hard time distinguishing the spiritual from the physical aspects of what it is to be human.

The bottom line in this argument is, in my view, concerned with *authenticity*. The difference between a person and a deep-fake copy of the person is that one of them is authentically human, the other is not, no matter how hyper real it may appear to be and no matter how good the objective test is that can't tell the difference between them.

Let me illustrate with an example. Imagine that I cut out a piece of paper the size of a fifty pound note. And a write "£50" on it and take it into a bank and ask them to change it for five £10 notes. Since this is a very poor 'simulation' of a fifty pound note, I'm not likely to get very far with this request. Suppose that I then take a photograph of a fifty pound note and print that at just the right size and take it into the bank. Visually, it will look like a fifty pound note (so it passes that 'objective' test), but as soon as they touch it, they will know it's a fake,

---

[6] I am grateful to Nick Chatrath for pointing out this error in the argument.

because fifty pound notes are printed on special paper.

Suppose now that I take this to the extreme. I find a printing machine and source the correct paper, and I manage to get copies of the original printing plates and I print off a high quality ('deepfake') fifty pound note, that is good enough to pass all the objective tests. Does its passing of the tests make it an authentic fifty pound note? Well it would certainly fool people into thinking it was a genuine fifty pound note. And they might treat it with the value that the genuine article has. But as soon as someone discovers that it was 'home made', it would loose its intrinsic value to them.

What is it that makes an authentic fifty pound note? Well, it does include having the correct materials (paper, inc, etc) and the correct printing plates, valid note sequence numbers and the expertise to make the forged bank note. But that in itself is not sufficient. In the UK bank notes are issued by the Bank of England, which was given the *authority* to do so from the Bank Charter Act 1844. So Government authority is required for the bank to be able to legally print and distribute fifty pound notes. This authority, in essence, is the real difference between the authentic and the deepfake fifty pound note.

In the same way, were we ever able to produce deepfake humans that were utterly convincing in looks and behaviour and difficult to distinguish from real humans, we should keep in mind that they will never be authentic humans, only simulations. Humans have a creator, a Person in *authority* who designed and made humans as they are with both body and spirit. No-one other than God has the capacity or the authority to create authentic humans.

Nevertheless, there may well come a time when we commonly treat hyper-real robots as though they were humans in many respects. I am less concerned about treating machines like humans than I am of treating humans like machines. The former raises the status of a machine, whilst the latter lowers the status of the human. There are some reasonable arguments in favour of raising the status of humalike machines. The most significant is that our treatment of those machines somehow mirrors our treatment of each other as humans, since the machines look like and behave like other humans. If we treat human-like machines badly, I fear that that would have an impact on the way we treat other humans. There has already been an online outcry over the videos which show a man apparently mistreating a human-like robot. This is a natural reaction, which I hope we will never loose.

9.4. Final words

So what have we made of the rise of the moral machine? We have shown that there is a need for some robots to possess a degree of moral competence, especially those robots that engage in social interactions with people. And we have explored some of the ways in which robots can be given this moral capacity. But what I hope is clear from our journey through this subject is that robots will always fall short of the capacity for human-level moral agency, no matter how hyper-real they are as simulations of humans. We should therefore never give our God given responsibility to be his moral agents on earth over to machines, and we should never put machines in positions of authority over humans. Robots should never be co-creators or architects of our moral landscape. Rather, they should be seen as morally naive at best, and be treated like children in that an adult human should always be responsible for them and their actions.

If we hold to this view, then despite the title of the book with its not-so-subtle reference to the movie 'Terminator 3: Rise of the Machines', we will not be heading for an Armageddon with our machine creations. Rather, we will be working towards a future in which humans and machines can collaborate, were machines can know and respect the moral boundaries of our societies, and can actively seek the genuine good and well being of humankind and all of God's creation.

.

Lightning Source UK Ltd.
Milton Keynes UK
UKHW010800161222
414034UK00006B/732